Keith Waterhouse, born in 1929, is the son of a Leeds costermonger. He worked in a cobbler's shop, an undertaker's and a garage before launching into journalism and becoming a writer.

Since then he has published eight novels: *There is a Happy Land* (1956), the brilliantly successful *Billy Liar* (1960), *Jubb* (1963), *The Bucket Shop* (1968), *Billy Liar on the Moon* (1975), *Office Life* (1978), *Maggie Muggins* (1981) and *In the Mood* (1983). He has also written extensively for the theatre, the cinema and television.

Keith Waterhouse is a frequent contributor to *Punch* and, since 1970, he has had his own column in the *Daily Mirror*. His *Mirror* columns have five times received national awards and in 1982 he won the Granada 'Columnist of the Quarter Century' award. *Fanny Peculiar* is his fourth collection of pieces: *Mondays, Thursdays* and *Rhubarb, Rhubarb and Other Noises* were both collections of his *Mirror* columns, and *The Passing of the Third Floor Buck*, the first of his *Punch* pieces.

D0610533

KEITH WATERHOUSE

Fanny Peculiar

Illustrated by Michael Heath

CORGI BOOKS

FANNY PECULIAR
A CORGI BOOK 0 552 12402 8

Originally published in Great Britain by
Michael Joseph Limited

PRINTING HISTORY

Michael Joseph edition published 1983
Corgi edition published 1984

Copyright © in this collection Keith Waterhouse 1983

Conditions of sale

1. This book is sold subject to the condition
that it shall not, by way of trade *or otherwise,*
be lent, re-sold, hired out or otherwise circulated
without the publisher's prior consent
in any form of binding or cover
other than that in which it is published
and without a similar condition including this condition
being imposed on the subsequent purchaser.
2. This book is sold subject to the Standard Conditions
of Sale of Net Books and may not be re-sold in the UK
below the net price fixed by the publishers for the book.

This book is set in 10/11 Palatino

Corgi Books are published by Transworld Publishers Ltd.,
Century House, 61-63 Uxbridge Road, Ealing, London W5 5SA

Made and printed in Great Britain by
Hunt Barnard Printing Ltd, Aylesbury, Bucks.

Introduction

This is a second collection of my pieces which originally appeared in *Punch*.

The first collection got by very well without an introduction. The only reason this lot has one is that I am also planning a collected edition of my introductions but am so far a couple of hundred pages short.

K.W.

Yanks for the Memory

Two thousand ex-GI's are planning a nostalgic return
to Bournemouth where they were stationed in the war.
BBC News

'Could I have some more coffee, dear?' asked Mr
Braithwaite, as he did every morning when he turned
to the leader page of *The Times*. His eyes, as always, did
not leave his newspaper.

'You surely can,' said Mrs Braithwaite, instead of
'Of course, dear' – her usual response in the morning
litany.

'And toast?'

'We're fresh out of toast, honey. I'll fix some.'

Mrs Braithwaite looked at the well-creased airmail
letter once again and popped some bread in the
toaster. Mr Braithwaite scanned the Letters to the
Editor and then asked his wife, as he always did, how
she proposed to spend the day.

'I guess I'll call the girls,' said Mrs Braithwaite.

'Girls?' Mr Braithwaite looked up from his paper.

'Uh huh.'

'But you don't know any girls!' said Mr Braithwaite. He was puzzled and slightly irritated. If his wife had told him that she was going to change her books at the public library or go to the flower-arranging class with Mrs Ormington-Cooper and Mrs Hulbertson, he could have turned to the share index in peace without even registering what she had said.

'Carol Ormington-Cooper and Angela Hulbertson, who else?' explained Mrs Braithwaite. 'I figured we'd go down town and take in a movie.'

Mr Braithwaite put down his newspaper altogether.

'What do you mean, "take in" a movie? Do you propose to give lodgings to a movie? Deceive a movie? Reduce the length or width of a movie on your sewing machine? Furthermore, why "movie" when you clearly mean film?'

'OK, wise guy, film.'

'And another thing,' pursued Mr Braithwaite, petulantly marmalading his fresh toast, 'why are you talking like one?'

'I don't dig,' said Mrs Braithwaite.

'Like a film. And a very bad film at that.'

'Oh yeah?' said Mrs Braithwaite. 'Sez you,' added Mrs Braithwaite.

Mr Braithwaite did not take the matter further. His wife was a prominent member of the Bournemouth Proscenium Players and it was very likely that she was in the throes of an amateur production of *Father of the Bride*. Given the slightest encouragement, she would probably rope him in the read the part of Spencer Tracy.

Mr Braithwaite went back to his *Times*. Mrs Braithwaite, under cover of a seed catalogue which had arrived in the same post as her airmail letter, read Hank's note for the twentieth time. After a while she said:

'Sweety-pie?'

'Yes, dear?'

'Do you remember when I used to date Lootenant Karminsky?'

Mr Braithwaite glowered. 'If you mean that damned Yank who used to shower you with nylons and gum while I was sitting it out in a blasted foxhole outside Sidi Barani, the answer is very well indeed. Why do you ask?'

Mrs Braithwite, to Mr Braithwaite's surprise, burst into song. The lyric, which was vaguely familiar to him, was to the effect that the Yanks were coming and that they wouldn't go back until it was over over there.

'Eleanor, are you feeling all right?'

'Sure! Swell! Oh boy!' observed Mrs Braithwaite. Slipping the airmail letter into her handbag, she added as casually as she could: 'He's planning a trip.'

'Is he, indeed? Then I hope he breaks his neck.'

'A trip *here*, honey lamb! I got the lowdown from a dame at City Hall. It seems a whole bunch of GI veterans are coming over from Stateside to paint the town red. Gee willikins,' said Mrs Braithwaite, 'will that be some party or will that be some party?'

'Will you be seeing this Karminsky chap?' asked Mr Braithwaite gruffly.

'Nope,' sighed Mrs Braithwaite. 'Way I reckon, you jest can't turn back the clock.'

'It's as well, dear. I don't know what you ever saw in the man. Frightful bounder, by all accounts.'

'I was lonesome,' said Mrs Braithwaite, 'and he was kinda cute. Anyhow, he talked my language. Y'know?'

Mrs Braithwaite did not telephone her friends Mrs Ormington-Cooper and Mrs Hulbertson. She went, as she often did, to Dorothy's Pantry in the town where she surprised the waitress by asking for a cawfee, easy on the cream, and a donut, hold the Jello. When the clock showed noon she walked to the

11

station where the London train was just coming in.

It was absurd, she told herself in retrospect, to have been on the lookout for the smart olive-drab jacket and trim fawn slacks of the GI she had known thirty-odd years ago. She was prepared for the receding hairline but not for the Brooks Brothers suit, nor the slim black documents case, nor the plastic identity tag attached to his lapel.

He recognized her at once. She had pinned on to her handbag the brass insignia of the US 34th Division which he had given her all those years ago, after that July Fourth hop at the Officers' Club.

'Eleanor?'

'You used to call me Kitten,' pouted Mrs Braithwaite. 'Still and all, it's good to see ya. How ya been, Hank?'

'Hank. Now that nomenclature is a whole lifestyle away. Namewise, anyone I relate with one-to-one calls me HK.' Karminsky touched his identity tag. 'It's a kind of work-ethic dynamic-energy projection we have, in-house. I'm into management now, did you know that?'

'Big deal,' said Mrs Braithwaite. 'Get you.'

'The use-of-initials concept identifies me as an authority figure. We have this interdisciplinary process scenario within the top-strata executive parameters. It's a kind of structured behavioural psychology print-out, read me?'

'Don't give me that boloney,' joked Mrs Braithwaite, uncertainly. It was his accent, she supposed. It would take some getting used to, as it had when he had first asked her to cut a rug with him at the Thanksgiving barn-dance.

They went into the buffet and had tea and biscuits. Mrs Braithwaite apologized that there was no blueberry pah.

Karminsky, saying that this was no hassle, explained

that he was into macrobiotics. He said that they were far out.

'How was your trip?' asked Mrs Braithwaite.

'Until customs completal, we had perfect lift-off. From London on in, I had a mobility problem. Transportation in that city is reaching totality, you better believe it.'

'Still and all, you finally made it. Over-sexed, over-paid and over here!'

'Lemme say this about that,' said Karminsky. 'It was great PR for the town of Bournemouth to extend this facility. Otherwise there was no way I could have gotten upfront credit mobility to finance the trip. I'm still operational on a break-even cost basis, but back home, we have downward growth at this time.'

'You sure said a mouthful,' said Mrs Braithwaite.

By way of banter, she asked him if he had any gum, chum. Karminsky replied that after analysis he was no longer oral dependent. He had, however, brought Mrs Braithwaite a volume called *Zen Skate-boarding*. He said that the post Watergate generation were really into this book, which unlocked their hang-ups.

'There's still not much to do in this burg,' Mrs Braithwaite said, when they had drunk their tea. 'Unless you'd like to cut a rug.'

'Excuse me?'

'You know – jitterbug. At the Palais.'

'Is that facility still viable here?' asked Karminsky. 'We've taken a revaluation of recreation-mobility since we moved into the conservation ballgame. We're more home-oriented.'

'I don't dig,' said Mrs Braithwaite.

'Is that so? You used to be into digging, or have you come through that experience? You were in a home economics situation, right?'

'I was in the Land Army, if that's what you mean,' said Mrs Braithwaite tartly.

13

They fell into an awkward silence. A tear trickled down Mrs Braithwaite's rouged cheek.

Karminsky coughed.

'I'm picking up signals,' he said.

'In a horse's ass you're picking up signals,' sniffed Mrs Braithwaite.

'Eleanor . . . ma'am . . . My value-judgement on this is that we're locked in a hostility situation here. We're not communicating, right? Maybe we're into different cultures. I don't want to lay a bad trip on you, honey, no way, but we don't relate. In any case, according to my prior background briefing I'm scheduled for a visit with the Bournemouth Chamber of Commerce . . .'

Mrs Braithwaite was putting the new *Radio Times* into its padded folder, embossed with the crest of the BBC and its motto, 'Nation Shall Speak Peace Unto Nation'. Mr Braithwaite was smoking his pipe.

Mrs Braithwaite spoke hesitantly. 'Honey . . . dear. Have I been behaving kinda – have I been behaving strangely?'

Mr Braithwaite judiciously packed down his pipe with the reamer she had given him for his birthday.

'I wouldn't say that, dear.'

'I feel as if I've been away on a long trip – a long journey,' said Mrs Braithwaite. 'But I'm back now, my dearest, I'm back.'

'Swell,' said Mr Braithwaite.

A Likely Story

What knickers in what glove compartment?

It's not my car.

It may well be my car, now that I look at it from this

14

angle, but those are not my knickers. Surely they're your knickers?

Yes, because don't you remember: when the dog chewed up my Kermit Squeezee-Sponge and I asked if you could spare me a bit of wash-leather or something to rub over the windscreen? And you said there was an old blue check duster in that biscuit tin under the sink where we keep the shoe-cleaning things?

I must have absent-mindedly gone to your dressing-table drawer and taken that pair of red satin knickers, then put it in the glove compartment thinking it was an old blue check duster.

Since you ask, no, I can't really see you wearing red satin knickers in a million years, especially that type. I'd qualify that even further and make it ten million years. Maybe that's one reason why we're not as close as we used to be.

However that doesn't alter the fact that the knickers were in your dressing-table drawer, where, not bothering to switch on the bedside lamp, I mistook them in the gathering dusk for a blue check duster.

How do I know? I expect you put them there yourself, after unwrapping them.

I know you have a short memory but surely you can remember getting a pair of red knickers for Christmas, among other perhaps more acceptable items? *I* certainly remember – I can remember your very words. 'Thank you very much but I couldn't wear these in a million years,' you said. 'I'll take them back to Janet Reger's when the shops open again and change them for a cardigan.' Then you must have popped them in your dressing-table drawer and not given them another moment's thought from that day to this.

All right. Joke over. Do you want to know what really happened?

You're not going to like this, I'm warning you.

Because it involves someone whose guts you hate.

Beresford, the office practical joker.

15

Of course you knew he was the office practical joker. That's why you hate his guts. Because he kept patting your bum at that dinner-dance we went to.

Well *he* thought it was a practical joke. Surely I'm not to be held responsible for my colleagues' offbeat sense of humour?

So. I can't prove anything, but I did notice when I set off home the other night that Beresford, the office practical joker, was hanging around the car-stack, where he'd no right to be since he doesn't drive. As you know.

Let me just get this straight. You're saying that if I try to tell you that Beresford, the office practical joker, somehow got into the car, somehow forced open the glove compartment, without breaking the lock, planted a pair of red satin knickers that he happened to have in his pocket, then somehow managed to lock the glove compartment again, you're going to see a solicitor, right?'

Then it's very fortunate indeed that that isn't what happened.

Beresford, the office practical joker, is only peripherally involved. The incident really centres on Carmichael.

Carmichael. I don't think you've met him. Has quite a reputation as the office conjuror. I've seen him do tricks with playing cards that would astound you. We all tell him he should take it up professionally. Listen: imagine, if you will, a bowl of goldfish, a wristwatch, an ordinary table napkin, the flags of all nations, an egg—

Did I mention tricks with glove compartments? Or sleight of hand with pairs of red knickers? Then until I do mention tricks with glove compartments and sleight of hand with pairs of red knickers, be so kind as to reserve judgement.

Where was I?

Good heavens.

You know that sensation one sometimes gets? Yes you do – the sensation that you know what someone's about to say? Déjà vu, isn't it? Well, I just had it then.

It was when I said, 'Where was I?' It suddenly brought something back to me. Sitting in the car and saying those very words. Well, not quite those very words but near enough. It wasn't 'Where was I?', it was 'Where am I?' or 'Who am I?' or something of that kind. I must have temporarily lost my memory.

No, I know that's not the same thing as déjà vu, but you know what I mean. Of course you do. Don't tell me you've never temporarily lost your memory and come round hearing yourself saying, 'Where am I?' or 'Who am I?'

I don't think I like your tone. I wouldn't *dream* of asking you to believe that I came round saying, 'Where

17

am I or who am I, and how did that pair of red knickers find its way into the glove compartment?' Had that been the case I would have mentioned it at the time.

The time I found myself sitting in the car asking, 'Where am I?' or 'Who am I?' as the case may be. The time I temporarily lost my memory.

Yes, well I was going to tell you about it but I forgot.

Red knickers don't come into it anywhere. I just got sidetracked by that moment of déjà vu or whatever it was.

I *am* getting back to the nitty-gritty. Beresford, the office practical joker, and Carmichael, the office conjuror, were how shall I put it, rather the worse for wear. Tired and emotional, as the phrase has it. Stinko. Three sheets in the wind.

You're right up to a point. Beresford, the office practical joker, didn't *used* to drink, but now he drinks like a fish. The only reason you don't know he drinks like a fish is because you won't have him in the house, because you hate his guts.

They were hanging around the car-stack. Beresford, the office practical joker, who doesn't drive, although he does now drink, was supporting Carmichael, the office conjuror, who both drives and drinks.

They'd been celebrating.

Does it matter what? Actually, since you ask, they'd been celebrating the news that Emerson, the office kleptomaniac, had just been appointed manager of the Bristol branch.

Didn't you? Oh, yes, the company keeps it hushed up. We've been asked not to talk about it. It's an illness. He takes pills for it.

Yes, that's perfectly correct, he did take charge of the Bristol branch two and a half years ago – in order, I might add in confidence, to save him the humiliation of being kept under surveillance by officers from Bow Street who suspected him of purloining washing from clothes-lines. But it was only a temporary appointment

18

until recently. As Emerson, the office kleptomaniac, will tell you if you ask him, he came back to Head Office to be confirmed as permanent Bristol manager. And promptly got pie-eyed with Beresford, the office practical joker, and Carmichael, the office conjuror.

By all means ring him up to congratulate him, if you know the Bristol STD code.

You may mention red knickers if you wish, but I cannot for the like of me see why you should want to. Have I accused Emerson, the office kleptomaniac, of stealing a pair of red knickers from Marks and Spencers and then stuffing them in the glove compartment of my car when he saw Beresford, the office practical joker, disguised as a policeman?

Very well then.

The only reason Emerson, the office kleptomaniac, comes into the story is that he was spending the night at the home of Carmichael, the office conjuror, before returning to Bristol by train. Carmichael, the office conjuror, was too drunk to drive. Beresford, the office practical joker, does not drive, as has been established. Foolishly, I volunteered to give them all a lift.

Now I am not going to weary you with the details of how Carmichael, the office conjuror, threw his latch-key out of the car window while we were crossing Chiswick flyover. He swore that when we arrived at his house he could produce it out of my glove compartment, and he is so damned clever – you know he's a member of the magic circle, don't you? Oh, yes. Vice-president – that we believed him, not knowing how sloshed he really was.

So. We arrive at Carmichael's, the office conjuror's, and I can see I don't have to tell you what's happened: we open the glove compartment and you've guessed it – no latch-key. Can't get in the house. Beresford, the office practical joker, has by now passed out cold and none of us knows where he lives, so I couldn't dump them all at *his* place. And I couldn't bring them back here because you hate Beresford's, the office practical joker's, guts.

So.

I'm cruising along Chiswick High Road wondering whether to drive them to a hotel or what the hell to do, when what should I see reflected in my diplights but this ankle length ball-gown. Containing, as it turned out, one stunning blonde, thumbing one lift.

Are you sure I haven't told you this story? I thought I had.

So naturally, being the gent I am, I stop, and in gets this blonde and sits in the front passenger seat, where the glove compartment is. Beresford, the office practical joker, Carmichael, the office conjuror, and Emerson, the office kleptomaniac, were all in the back, sleeping it off.

Now as you know, there's a light in the glove compartment, which happened to be open because we'd been searching for Carmichael's, the office conjuror's, latch-key; so I was able to get a good look at her face. Hello, I thought, I've seen you before darling.

And do you know who it was?

I can see you're not going to get it. Of all people, it was none other than Jamieson, the office transvestite. Not all that much of a coincidence, because as you probably know he lives in the same street as Carmichael, the office conjuror, and Bates, the office security manager.

'Thank God it's you four,' says Jamieson, the office transvestite, 'because I'm in dead trouble . . .'

Spring with Monicker

Finding a name for a new car is not straightforward.
Either you hit upon someone else's idea or find that it has been used before.

Guardian

'Riley,' said Lamprey, Marketing.

'Been done,' said Eames, Forward Thinking.

'Jowett.'

'Been done.'

'Bentley.'

'Been done. You're beginning to flag a bit, Peter. Why don't you lie down for a bit and get some shut-eye?'

Gilfillian, Publicity, fanned smoke from his watering eyes with *Everyman's Dictionary of Fictional Characters*. 'A good kip is what we could all do with,' he yawned. 'I've just got this word Baskerville going round and round in my head.'

'Baskerville. That's not a make of a car, it's a type-face,' Eames said, ploddingly.

'I know. That's what I'm saying.'

'Or Sherlock Holmes's dog,' said Paget, Advertising.

'The dog that didn't bark in the night,' intoned Isinglass, Promotions, balancing a pencil in one of the furrows on his brow.

'Rover,' said Lamprey.

'Been done,' said Eames. 'Let's kick proper names around a bit more, shall we?'

'I'll tell you what,' said Paget, snapping his fingers. 'Pegasus.'

'That's not a proper name.'

'Bloody *Cortina* isn't a proper name!'

'As it so happens, it is,' said Eames. 'But let it pass. The point I'm making is, I thought we'd agreed to keep off animals.'

'We agreed to keep off different makes of *sheep*,' said Paget, after exhaling heavily and rolling his eyes

heavenwards. 'Nobody, so far as I am aware, has so far given the thumbs-down to winged mythological creatures based on *horses*.'

'Well I'm giving it now,' said Eames. 'For one thing your trademark would look like a petrol sign – '

'So we're in the same business, so what?'

'So let's call the bloody car Esso and go home to bed, if that's how you feel!' flared Eames. 'Anyway, Pegasus has been done.'

'Then tell me something that *hasn't* been done!' snapped Eames.

'Norris.'

'Been done.'

'Not Morris, *Norris*!' screamed Lamprey, thumping the table. 'As in he who changes sodding trains! If you've no ideas of your own, Roger, you might have the courtesy to pay proper attention to other people's!'

'When anyone produces an original idea – just one,' retorted Eames icily, 'I will give it all the attention in the world. In the meantime, I may not be all that bright but I am not bloody deaf. I *know* you said Norris, Peter, and I reiterate that Norris has been done.'

'Where? When?'

'Luton, let me see nineteen-thirty-six,' Eames recited, screwing up his eyes as in concentration. 'The Norris

Eight. Twin camshaft job, celluloid windows. Got bought out by Vauxhall.'

'He's bluffing,' murmured Paget.

Gilfillian had abandoned his *Dictionary of Fictional Characters* in favour of a volume of the *Encyclopedia Britannica*. 'All right, let *me* give you one,' he said. 'And tell me if *I'm* bluffing. Oliver.'

'Oliver who?' asked Eames.

'Are we trying to think up a name for a car, or are we playing knock-knock?' asked Isinglass mildly, without removing his pencil from his right nostril where he had lodged it with a view to swinging it idly backwards and forwards, like a pendulum.

'Oliver Evans,' said Gilfillian. 'Now you've got to ask me who Oliver Evans was.'

Nobody rose to the bait. Paget had closed his eyes and was probably asleep. Lamprey wrote the word 'FROD' on his pad and stared at it dully.

'He ran an amphibious steam dredge through the streets of Philadelphia in 1804,' pursued Gilfillian after a suitable pause. 'And if you don't believe me – '

'It doesn't matter whether we believe you or not,' said Eames. 'It's a sodding awful name.'

'Frod,' said Lamprey. 'I know it's not *quite* there, but – '

Ignoring Lamprey, Eames continued: 'Subliminally, it stinks. I mean, Christ almighty, what's the first thing Oliver suggests? Asking for more. More what? More oil, more petrol? It's terrible.'

'Frod, then,' said Lamprey.

'Look,' said Gilfillian. 'If you're so bloody smart, why don't you *think* up a name?'

'Bloody *Frod!*'

'Lola,' said Eames.

There was a stunned silence. 'It sounds,' said Lamprey sulkily, at last, 'like a Wardour Street whore.'

'It happens to be my mother's name,' said Eames icily. 'If you care to step out into the street, I'm sure we can discuss your objections to it further.'

The raised voices had woken Paget up again. 'You know,' he said, stretching elaborately, 'whoever suggested proper names in the first place has cost us our dinner and a good night's sleep. Why don't we get back to allegorical names?'

'So long as they're not horses sprouting wings,' said Eames. 'And so long as Prattface here doesn't start bringing up Allegro again.'

'If you're referring to me by any remote chance,' said Lamprey, dangerously calm, 'I have brought up Allegro, which for your information is *not* allegorical—'

'Neither is Pegasus, if we're going into dictionary flaming definitions,' said Paget. 'It's mythological.'

'I was about to say, I have brought up Allegro precisely once this evening, and that was for one purpose and one purpose only – to illustrate that many excellent car names begin with an A. Allegro, Austin, Alpine, the list is endless.'

'Go on, then,' said Gilfillian.

'Go on what?'

'What's your suggestion?'

'Frod.'

'Bollocks,' said Eames.

'That's a good name for a car,' murmured Isinglass, abandoning an effort to make his pencil adhere to his index finger by its point.

'Talking of good names for cars,' said Gilfillian, staring abstractedly at his watch, then shaking it, 'the Japs did some research into the perfect name for an English model, and came up with Cedric.'

'Typical,' said Paget. 'I'm sure if we wanted a name for a Jap car the computer would come up with Hiroshima.'

'Can we cut down the chitter-chatter?' pleaded Eames rapping the table. 'Let's see what we've got on the short list so far. Madrid. Who suggested Madrid?'

'I did,' confessed Isinglass, 'but I was pissed at the

time. It was after lunch, if you remember. Tell me, when you see double, is it your liver?'

'It's sitting in a smoky room for fifteen hours, trying to think up a smart-arse name for a bloody car, when the obvious one is probably staring us in the face,' said Paget.

'Like what?'

'Like how the bloody hell do I know? Granada.'

'Been done,' said Eames automatically.

'How about London Weekend?' asked Isinglass, deadpan.

'Actually,' said Lamprey, 'London Weekend isn't a bad name for a car.'

'Don't talk so bloody stupid,' said Eames.

'Listen,' said Lamprey heavily. 'If you speak to me like that just once more, I am personally going to flatten your big, red ugly nose. You won't consider Frod and you won't consider London Weekend. What the bloody hell *will* you consider?'

Gilfillian was staring at his watch again. His eyes finally focused. It was 4.37 am.

'Bedtime, I think,' said Gilfillian.

Eames banged the table.

'I *like* it!' he shouted. 'Bedtime! It's got everything! Sex! Everything!'

'Sounds like a box of chocolates to me,' sneered Paget.

'London Weekend Assortment,' said Lamprey. 'That's even better, and if you say one word, Eames, just one bloody word, I shall kick your teeth in.'

Eames rose stiffly and put on his jacket. 'Meeting adjourned,' he said.

Isinglass, pocketing his pencil, affected to ponder. 'Meeting Adjourned Two Thousand. Meeting Adjourned Convertible. No. Doesn't grab me.'

'Same time tomorrow,' said Eames.

25

Fanny Peculiar

Northerners striving for social improvement by adopting educated southern speech are likely to be pulled up by their friends for inaccurate vowel sounds, says Mr Graham Nixon, a lecturer in English language, at Sheffield University . . . For example, in trying to pronounce a phrase like 'good luck' in what phoneticians call received pronunciation, they pronounce 'good' with the vowel sound of the southern 'cup', and 'luck' with the vowel sound of 'book'.

Guardian

See Janet. See John. Janet and John have a new pappy. See the pappy. The pappy's name is Fadge.

Fadge is called Fadge because Janet and John like fadge to eat. They like it better than bahl's-eyes or hambags. They buy fadge at the tack-shop. Do you like fadge?

John has an old ranning-pamp. Can you see the pamp? Fadge can see the pamp. 'Waff!' barks Fadge. 'Waff! Waff!'

Janet has a cream ban. Can you see Janet's ban? Fadge sees the ban. 'Waff!' barks Fadge. 'Waff! Waff!'

John throws the ranning-pamp into a bash. 'Fetch, Fadge, fetch!' cries John.

Fadge rans into the bash and fetches the pamp. Janet pals the pamp from Fadge and gives him the ban. Fadge eats the ban. What fan!

Janet and John go to school. See the school. See Miss Clatterback. Miss Clatterback is Janet and John's teacher.

John is gad at sams. He can count up to a hundred. Are you gad at sams?

Janet is not gad at sams. She cannot even add wan and wan. But she is gad at elocution. Are you gad at elocution?

'How match wadd cad a waddchack chop if a waddchack cad chop wadd?' recites Janet. She is learning to speak as if she came from Sussex or Surrey.

Do you cam from Sussex or Surrey? Do you speak like Janet? Of course you do. But Janet cams from Haddersfield. Clever Janet, to speak as if she cams from Sussex. Haddersfield is in Yorkshire. See the chimneys.

'Very gad, Janet,' said Miss Clatterback. 'Now let ass hear John say it.'

'How mooch wood could a woodchuck chop if a woodchuck could chop wood?' recites John. Oh dear.

'Everytime you open your mouth you pat your fat in it,' scolds Miss Clatterback. 'Does your mather teach you to speak like that?'

'No, miss,' pats in Janet. 'It's our Dad. He tells us off for speaking fanny.'

'There's nothing fanny about gad pronanciation,' says Miss Clatterback. 'John mast stay in after school and brash ap his vowels.'

Poor John.

Daglas is the school bully. He is waiting for Janet at the bass-stop. See Daglas skalking at the bass-stop. He means to bally Janet.

Daglas has a backet of mad. He means to chack mad at Janet. John is not with her. Do not see John. John is with Miss Clatterback, brashing ap his pronanciation. When Daglas chacks mad at Janet, John will not be there to panch him.

'Ullo, Janet,' says Daglas.

'Hallo, Daglas,' says Janet.

'Ecky thump, don't you talk funny?' says Daglas.

'Hecky thamp yourself,' says Janet. 'I'm not like sam folk – I don't whant everywan to know I cam from

Haddersfield, even if ather people do.'

'What's opp wi' Uddersfield?' asks Daglas, taking a handfal of mad from his backet.

'What's ap with Haddersfield? My mother says it's common,' says Janet, 'and if you chack that mad at me, you big bully, I'll kick your bam.'

Daglas throws the mad at Janet bat rans off before she can kick his bam. See Daglas ran off. See the mad on Janet's tammy. Janet starts to blabber.

Poor Janet.

See John with Miss Clatterback. Miss Clatterback throws the blackboard rabber at John. See the blackboard rabber hit John.

'Wonce again,' says Miss Clatterback.

'It should be a good stud at Goodwood,' recites John.

Miss Clatterback throws her cashion at John. See the cashion hit John.

'Wonce again,' says Miss Clatterback.

'It shad be a good stad at Goodwood,' repeats John.

Miss Clatterback pals John's ear. Paint John's ear red.

'Wonce again.'

'Ow! It shad be a gad stad at Gadwadd.'

'By George, I think he's got it!' exclaims Miss Clatterback. 'Now wonce again, what kind of stad shad it be at Gadwadd?'

Miss Clatterback raffles John's hair.

'It shad be a gad stad at Gadwadd.'

'There! Now ran off home, and never again let me hear you attering your vowels as if you were brought up in the gatter.'

'No, Miss Clatterback,' sniffles John, drying his eyes.

Clever John.

See Janet and John having their sapper. They are having sapper with their mather and Dad. See Janet and John's mather and Dad. Their Dad is the one in the vest and braces.

For their sapper, Janet and John are having babble and squeak followed by bread and batter padding and castard.

Janet and John's Dad has a big mag of tea. 'Pass me t'sugar, our Janet,' he says.

'Pardon, our Dad?' asks Janet.

'He means the shagger,' says John.

Janet and John's Dad fetches John an almighty clout across the lag-hole. Paint John's other ear red.

'Thou toffee-nosed little sod, what have I told thee abaht talking as if thy hed a plum in thy mouth!' roars Janet and John's Dad.

'You mean a plam, our Dad,' says Janet. Janet and John's Dad swipes her across the lag-hole too. See Janet blabber again.

'Our Janet and our John!' cries Janet and John's mather, 'Ran apstairs and play. I whant a whord whith your father.'

See Janet and John ran apstairs.

See the mather and father of all rows break out downstairs. 'Now see here, you great agly lamp of lard!' snaps Janet and John's mather. 'How can I bring up my kiddies to speak nicely when there's you carrying on like Lady Chatterley's Lavver? In future, we'll have sam gad manners at table. And anather thing, you're going to start having a glarss of whine whith your sapper instead of that disgusting mug of tea!'

'Owt else?' asks Janet and John's Dad salkily.

'Yes! There'll be no more Sandy dinners whaiting for you when you roll back from the pab. From now on, you'll get Sandy branch!'

'Oh, ah will, will ah? *That* for your Sunday brunch!'

See Janet and John's Dad throw his sapper in the fireplace.

See Janet and John playing apstairs. 'Shall we play at mathers and fathers now?' says Janet.

'All right,' says John. 'You start.'

'What bladdy time of night do you call this to cam home?' asks Janet.

'Oh, bagger off, wamman!' says John graffly.

Loose Leaf

They say all your life swims before you as you float to the ground.

I do hope so. It has been, for me, a wonderful, crowded life, full of enchantment. To recall but a fraction of those far-off golden moments as I am wafted down beyond the park railings and brought to rest in the gutter to await the shovel and brush of the Royal Borough of Kensington and Chelsea Cleansing Department, would be to re-live an age so remote from the present day, with its inhospitable temperature of 45°F (7°C) and its uncouth frontal trough with a NW wind moderate to fresh, that it seems like a dream. But then I am one of that dwindling generation of leaves fortunate enough to have lived through the now legendary, carefree summer of 1981, and before it that magic, captivating spring, also of 1981 when the world was full of promise and – provided the caterpillars didn't get you – all was possible.

It was in that by gone era (I steadfastly decline to name the exact month, for that would be to sound older than I feel!) that I first saw the light. Our rather grand family name was *Quercus Pedunculata* but except on the most formal occasions when a professor of botany might come along and point at us with his stick, we were known simply, and to all and sundry, as 'those oak leaves'.

We were a large, madcap, happy bunch – perhaps two or three thousand of us all clinging higgledy-piggledy to the dear old rambling branches of the dear old rambling tree that, all through those blissful seasons, was our only home. We were comfortably enough off – indeed, by present-day standards I suppose it could be said we wanted for nothing. There was dew in plenty and every so often there would be a scattered shower or some such treat, almost invariably

followed by a sunny interval – harbinger of the
shimmering summer yet
to come.

We were lucky enough,
touch wood, to come from
robust and healthy stock
(though inevitably in so
large a family one or two
of us were taken quite
young – usually by school-
children on nature walks)
and so, unchecked by
cuckoo-spit, fungi or stem
gall, we thrived like ever-
greens, the only cloud on
the horizon being that
we were in fact deciduous.
But the horizon was far,
far away, farther even than the pale yellow dawn with
which each long and perfect day began, or the burnished
sunset with which it ended. In those first great
moments of the long-ago, to be deciduous was to live
for ever.

Our address – the second oak tree along past the
men's lavatories as you sway in the direction of the
Albert Memorial – was perhaps no longer as fashion-
able as it had once been many seasons ago before some
of our neighbours had the misfortune to go down
with elm-blight. But it suited us: we were well out of
the path of box-kites and model gliders that so much
plagued our wealthier relatives who had put down
their roots in the rich soil near the Round Pond; and if
the occasional Iranian student attempted to carve
'LONG LIVE NEW SHAH' in the trunk of our shabby
but comfortable quarters, there was usually a friendly
bobby on hand to pin him to the park railing and knee
him in the groin while radioing for a van. That was in

31

gentler, sunnier times before God-fearing trees were left to the mercy of every shaft of lightning or urinating dog, and when the young leaves, drunk on sunlight, were so arrogantly fearless of the compost heap which awaits us all that they could declare themselves bored of living up a tree and would plan great expeditions on the April winds.

But we were not really bored: far from it. Those halcyon days, in truth, were filled with activity. I confess that in my cantankerous old age I grow impatient when I hear holly leaves in the bush next door whining that they have nothing to do but snag the sleeves of passers-by and stare at berries. We had no red, shining berries to divert us – we had acorns, of course, but they are dull company – and most of us dwelled on branches so high that sleeve-snagging was out of the question, even had we had the constitution for it.

No matter: we were a resourceful family of leaves and we made our own amusements. We found so much to occupy us that we were at it from morning till night. For example, there was breathing: we used to do a lot of that, not only to assist the photosynthesis process vital to the health of any tree by the absorption of carbon dioxide which is then broken down into its component parts of oxygen and carbon, but because it was fun. Or, given a light breeze, we would sometimes sway about. Or, if it rained, get wet, with the delicious prospect of gradually becoming dry again after it stopped. Then there was bouncing up and down, occasioned by a bird landing on one's branch and then taking off again. I had that experience quite often, I am delighted to say.

Much of the day, of course, was taken up with the routine business of turning very slowly indeed on one's petiole to face the sun – a somewhat sedentary occupation after the novelty wore off, I must confess, but one that was usually enlivened by some diversion or other – an insect crawling along one's stem, perhaps, or an unexpected drop of water landing on one from a fellow-leaf higher up the tree. By the time darkness fell, we would be so exhausted that all we wanted to do was to curl up our serrations and sleep, until the chirruping of the blackbird warned us to prepare for the new excitements of a new day.

And what red-letter days they were, so very many of them! I have lost count of the number of times a father out walking with his offspring has paused, pointed up to us breathing or swaying on our boughs, and announced, 'That is an oak tree.'

Asked by his marvelling progeny how he could possibly deduce such a thing, the father would invariably say, 'Well, because of the acorns.' Preening ourselves, and turning imperceptibly to bask in flattery as we would turn to bask in the sun, we leaves would wait for what we knew would come next.

'But even if there aren't any acorns, darling, you can still always tell. Shall I tell you how you can tell? *Because of the oak's crinkly leaves.*'

Never mind that instead of 'crinkly leaves' he should more accurately have said, 'Leaves of runcinate outline.' Never mind that common sycamores nearby would jeer, 'Cor, it must be very nice having your leaves recognized by a punter what's just smashed a dozen mushrooms to smithereens because he thought they was toadstools.' Our cup was full. We were young and gay, and the world was talking about us. It was high summer, nothing could go wrong, and it would be like that for ever and a day.

The crash came suddenly. There had been warnings – I cannot, with hindsight, say that there hadn't. All the acorns had fallen. We didn't care. That, we cynically said to one another, was the function of acorns. Besides, there was so much else to think about. There were breathing parties to go to – as many as five or six a day as the season wore on – and swaying weekends to be organized. If the breathing was getting ominously faster and the swaying becoming slightly hysterical, we didn't notice. How could we, when we were so busily burning the candle at both ends?

One morning we began to notice that we were all turning yellow. 'Jaundice,' said a wit, but the joke fell flat. We, who could not grow old, were growing old. The impossible was happening. The cloud that had been for so long on that far horizon was now, in an instant, dreadfully near, and we saw now that it was a cloud of smoke. Bonfire smoke.

People passed by and remarked how beautiful we looked in our new colours. What the more fanciful among them called nature's palette was, however, simply a question of one's carotenoids being made visible by decomposition of the chlorophylls. It was the beginning of the end.

One by one the dancing leaves began to flutter, pirouette, and fall, to be swept away next morning by the council dust-cart. Then a N by NW wind mainly fresh or strong rustled through our branches – only a passing gust, but when it had gone, it had taken the secret of eternal youth with it.

I am alone now, hanging by a thread from my bare branch. Down there, in the last wine-drop of winter sunshine, my fallen fellow-leaves look all golden, as if they are still living in that endless summer. Is there an after-cycle for deciduals? I shall know, soon enough.

Pietro Pan

LONDON CASINO. 437 6877. Twice Daily at 2.15 & 7.30
SUSANNAH YORK, RON MOODY

34

PETER PAN
By Eduardo De Filippo
Until Jan 14, £4, £3, £2.50, £1.50.

Standard Theatre Guide

A third floor flat in Naples. Rocco and Maria Darling are preparing to go out for the evening. The children – Michele, Wendy and Giovanni – are being put to bed by the dog, Bambinaia.

MARIA   Cretin! Fool! Imbecile! I tell you there was a face at the window.

ROCCO   The woman is crazy. (*To the children*) At last, it is out in the open. Your mother is mad. We are three floors up and she sees a face at the window!

MARIA   It was there!

ROCCO   Where is my revolver?

MICHELE   Why do you want your revolver, papa?

ROCCO   I am going to shoot the dog.

MARIA   Monster! As well as being a fool you are a murderer! What has the dog done to you?

ROCCO   Just now, I tried to give the dog some medicine. It was the same medicine you wanted my children to take.

MARIA   Now they are your children. When they do something wrong they are my children.

ROCCO   If you'll excuse me, there would certainly be something wrong if I left the children in your hands. You are trying to poison them. That is why the dog will not take the medicine. I am very sorry but I cannot allow you to poison my children, just because you think you saw a face at the window and you are afraid they might fly away. Either the dog tries the medicine first or I will shoot it. This is a matter for the dog.

Still squabbling, Rocco and Maria go out of the room, dragging the dog between them. Suddenly the night-lights over the beds go out, and a dancing, prancing twinkle – the fairy Campanello –

begins darting noisily about the room. The window is blown open, and Pietro Padella flies in.

PIETRO You have a strange sense of humour if I may say so, Campanello! I ask you to find my shadow and be discreet about it, and you make enough noise to waken a corpse! Please! Why don't you tear down the wardrobe and have done with it?

WENDY *(waking up)* Boy, why are you shouting?

PIETRO When I was a child, I lived in a stinking room in the Via Blatta. There were nine of us, including my mother, God rest her soul. She was a washerwoman. She did her best for us, there was never a better mother who ever lived, but the plain truth of the matter is that we were very poor. Each Sunday she made a pizza in a dustbin-lid and it had to last us the week. What pizzas they were! My mother didn't squeeze the tomato paste from a bottle, you know, she made it with her hands from tomatoes we had picked from the gutter outside Don Pepperoni's the greengrocer. And the paste had to be just so! She would rub a little olive oil on her hands so as to get the correct consistency. And this was most important, she would always rub the dustbin-lid with a clove of garlic before commencing to cook. I tell you, as a fact, we had the finest pizzas in all Napoli. But one day the lid of the dustbin was stolen and we had nothing to eat. I remember that day as if it were yesterday. My mother took us to the Via Calabritto and sold our shadows for a few lira to Donna Lucia Merletto, the lacemaker. While I was waiting outside the shop I became bored, so I ran away to live among the fairies.

MICHELE You say all this to my sister, Don Pietro, but you ignore us, her brothers. Excuse me, but you are not very polite. If you had spoken to me about the matter I could have told you at once. Your shadow is over there. The dog has been using it as a blanket.

36

GIOVANNI But now our father intends to shoot the dog and we shall have nothing to live for, nothing. Will you teach us to fly also, and then we can teach him a lesson he will not forget by following you to the Never Land?

PIETRO That will be your reward, my friends.

While Pietro Padella is teaching the children to fly, Rocco Darling storms back into the room, followed by his wife Maria and the dog Bambinaia.

ROCCO Bravo! Now I see that I am living in a circus! It is a good thing after all that I could not tie my tie this evening, or I would have gone out of the house and missed a remarkable sight. My own children, the children of my blood, flying around like budgerigars! Well, it is very plain indeed what is happening in this house. My wife is mad and now you are all trying to drive me mad also.

MARIA I told you there was a face at the window but you would not listen. You never listen.

ROCCO I am going to kill him. First I will shoot the dog and then I will kill this – this flying boy, this monstrosity!

PIETRO To die will be an awfully big adventure.

Before Rocco can carry out his threat the Lost Boys fly into the room.

ROCCO Oh, please! This is a hotel! Allow me to take your coats – I want you all to be as comfortable as possible! Permit me to say I am sorry there are not enough beds but I am sure arrangements can be made. If there is anything you require, please have no hesitation in asking my wife, Donna Maria. You will find she is very accommodating to strangers.

MARIA What do you mean by that?

ROCCO For twenty three years now you have

been laughing at me behind my back. You pretend to be a faithful wife but as soon as I am out of the house, or as soon as you think I am out of the house, you throw open the window to admit all the guttersnipes of Napoli. And not content with that you want to poison my children so they will not have the misfortune to witness the disgraceful way you are behaving. Whore! Harlot!

MARIA (*throwing her wedding ring at him*) You make me tired. (*To Wendy*) I don't mind your friends coming into the house in spite of all your father says, but won't you introduce them to your mother? After all, I am not yet a piece of furniture although I am treated as one.

TOOTLINO Forgive us, Donna Maria, but we are the Lost Boys. Please overlook this intrusion, but with your permission we have come to ask your daughter if she will come and keep house for us, and tell us stories.

WENDY Why should I do anything for you? For years I would work my fingers to the bone. The stories you ask for would come out of my living heart. I would polish your furniture with all the love I have, each day I would scrub your clothes with my life blood. And at the end there would be nothing. Nothing.

Capitano Uncino enters, carrying a ragu *in an earthenware pot and pursued by a crocodile.*

CAPITANO Donna Maria! Allow me to say you are looking marvellous this evening! And you, Don Rocco, my friend! You are a very lucky fellow, you know!

ROCCO Permit me, Capitano Uncino, I am not in the mood for your light-hearted conversation on this occasion. Please to excuse yourself and take your crocodile with you. First my house is a circus and now it

38

is a zoological garden.

CAPITANO   He follows me everywhere. He bit off my arm, you know. This was many years ago. You must allow me to tell you the circumstances. When I was a little boy, I lived in a stinking room in the Via –

MARIA   We have no time for your stories now, Capitano. What is in the pot?

CAPITANO   I have made a *ragu* for Don Pietro and the Lost Boys. Having no mother, they don't know how dangerous it is to eat rich, damp *ragu*. They will die!

MARIA   I should think so, the way you have prepared the dish! That is no way to make a *ragu*.

CAPITANO Donna Maria, I should apologize a thousand times for contradicting you, but second only to you I make the best *ragu* in Napoli. First it is essential to fry the onions at the proper temperature, and then –

MARIA   (*To Rocco*) Will you stand by me and let him tell me how to make a *ragu* in my own house? You do not fry the onions first. Any child knows that. The first thing you must do is to give your attention to the pan, by taking a little knob of butter –

GIOVANNI   The fairy Campanello has eaten some of the *ragu* and is very ill.

MARIA   There! That proves what I have been saying all along.

ROCCO   Yes! You would like us to believe that, wouldn't you? Murderess! The fact is that the fairy Campanello did not eat the *ragu*, she drank the medicine that was meant for my children! There is the proof I have been looking for.

MARIA   Excuse him. Capitano Uncino, he is out of his mind.

WENDY   In any event Campanello is dead.

PIETRO   If I may say so, she is not yet dead, but her light is growing faint. Whenever a family quarrels, a

39

fairy dies. We can only save her if we pluck the venom out of our hearts and say to ourselves that we believe in families. (*To the audience*) Do you believe in families? Say quickly that you believe!

AUDIENCE Si.

THE CURTAIN FALLS

Notes from a Hole in the Ground

For eight years a man hiding from the police lived in a hole only six feet long and two feet deep under the floorboards of his council house.

Daily Telegaph

Day 2819
(Or Day 2735 as it might be if, round about that time I could not sleep too well owing to noise from next-door rats, I was counting one day as two owing to waking up in the middle of night and thinking it was morning, then nodding off after breakfast, thinking it was supper. Got in such a state that wife finally called in doctor who lowered down sick-note for my nerves,

also put me on Mogadon. But he says I will never be a hundred percent fit until I have been transferred to a more modernized hole on one of the new estates, however there is long waiting list so it is useless making application. Trouble where we are now is that foundations of these houses are only wafer-thin, they are jerry-built, you can hear every sound from drains etc, and neighbours have no consideration, flushing toilet at all hours God sends. Some people live like pigs. Council should do something but they won't.)

Uneventful day. Police still not come.

Day 2822
There is definitely rising damp in this hole, you cannot tell me it is condensation. It is all the same under this class of house, they are like Niagara Falls.

Wish now we had put a deposit down on that little bungalow we once looked at, instead of lashing out on holidays in Benidorm. It could be wax-sealed parquet I was lying under now if I had done sensible thing, not rough floorboards. Also, if it is your own place, you do not mind spending a few bob on improvements. First off, I would have proper concrete base to lie on, not just earth, and this I would cover with adhesive non-slip composition tiles. Then, after smoothing edges of hole and bonding cracks with Polyfilla, I would line walls with $5/8$" fibreboard painted with two coats polyurethane gloss in simulated antique oak. To complete homely touch I would have a lowered egg-box ceiling fitment with concealed lighting, as well as making a feature of illuminated fish-tank on brackets above laminated folding work-top with rounded edges.

But even if it was worth outlay when it is not our own hole, try asking council for permission to do these things, it is always a case of, 'Oh, if we let one tenant put in double-glazing under floorboards, they will all want it.' But will council lift a finger to improve hole themselves? Not them, it takes them all their time to put washer on tap.

Next time wife pokes shredded food through cracks I will tell her to ask rent collector if council will at least consider lagging hole with fibreglass, otherwise it is all round to health inspector.

Police still not come.

Day 2825
Thursday, I think.

Kept awake by squeaking floorboards, it is public scandal. All they need is nailing down properly where I had to dislodge them to squeeze into hole, but council will not come and do job despite frequent requests. Good mind to write to Harold Wilson.

Doze off. Wake up again. Floorboards still squeaking. It is somebody pacing up and down with heavy tread. This means either police have come or it is rent collector. If it is police they would be shining torch through knot-hole, not walking up and down. If it is rent collector it cannot be Thursday as I thought, it must be Friday. If it is Friday it is Day 2826. How time flies.

. *Later:* Wife taps out message. (Have both learned Morse while I have been down here. She can now stamp on floorboards at speeds up to 60 words per min.) It was rent collector all right. She raised question of lagging hole with fibreglass and by all accounts he went spare, accusing wife of sub-letting hole to lodger, or even worse, keeping rabbits or similar pets down it, both being contrary to council regulations. Wife swore to God, truthfully so far as she knew, that this was not the case. I have never told her that I have got the dog down here with me. She thinks it ran away in 1974.

Hearing a bark (wife thinks I have a bad cough, which truth to tell I have owing to rising damp), rent collector refused to believe her and threatened to bring round housing manager plus workforce with crowbars, but at death wife managed to persuade him that she merely wants to insulate hole for use as a dinette, being as how there is now fungus sprouting out of kitchen dining-recess and same is going to wife's chest. I tell her she would be better off moving down here with me where we could be one big happy family, but she will have none of it, apparently she has these giddy spells if she has to live in the dark for six months or more.

Wife was stamping out in Morse what rent collector said about insulating hole for dinette purposes – still improper use, according to him – when message became garbled owing to neighbours thumping on wall with poker. Flipping nuisance they are, wish we could get eviction order on grounds of harassment to resident of hole. Police still not come.

Day 2827
Wife stamped out message to effect that there is new law whereby council tenants can buy their own houses. Could not ascertain asking price, as at this point wife's Morse-tappings on floorboards subtly changed into Waverley Two Step (pas de basque towards partner, LF, RF, LF, glissade), indicating that someone was at door and she was pretending for their benefit to be practising for her old-tyme dancing medal, this being well known to be her hobby. Resounding progressive waltz turn on floorboards (followed by uncalled-for hammering on party wall by neighbours) gave me welcome coded information that caller was not police as feared, but wife's mother who does not know I am down here, she has been told I went out looking for dog seven and a half years ago and have yet to return. Was therefore left in peace to ruminate on news given to me by wife.

If price is right and I buy house, I could extend hole as far as boundary wall, always assuming no snags as regards getting planning permission. This should give me at least ten extra feet of hole to play with. I could also deepen it a bit one of these fine days, but must not run before I can walk. By extending outwards, I could make room L-shaped hole for living in, plus small patio with aluminium-framed sliding glass doors, if same are available two feet deep. This would be useful for walking dog, plus growing own mushrooms. As owner occupier, it might be worthwhile getting quotation for guaranteed damp course. Would certainly need it before lashing out on fitted carpet. Wonder if I could get improvement grant. It is worth thinking about. Police still not come.

Day 2849

Drainpipe running through hole makes first-class Morse-tapper when banged with corned beef tin, but unfortunately message apparently resounds in neighbours' bathroom. Today, after I had asked wife why she think police not come after nearly eight years, and expecting her usual reply that they are biding their time, I was surprised to hear, 'Don't worry, sunshine, they will be here soon enough,' reverberating through drainpipe loud and clear. It is the neighbours. They have learned Morse. My days therefore numbered. No longer have heart to measure up for built-in hardwood shelves and wardrobe fitment.

Day 2850

Hear siren. Police come. Hear neighbours tell police I have been living under floorboards for eight years. Hear police laugh. Hear gruff voice saying, 'Pull other one, it has got bells on it.' Hear police drive away. Hear neighbours say, 'That does it then, we will move out of the bloody neighbourhood, you cannot hear yourself think what with that maniac banging away on the pipes like James Cagney in *Each Dawn I Die*.' Hear wife practising Schottische (Temps levé on RF and close LF, slight body turn to L). Realize after while that it is not Schottische at all, but Morse for 'It is all right, you can come out now.' Reply that will wait until coast is clear. Police might come back. Besides, have just discovered comfortable position to lie in. No rick in neck for once.

Day 13,809
Uneventful day, or perhaps night. Police not come.

The Form of Marriage

The government is considering appointing a Minister for Marriage to help keep families together as the basis of a caring society.
Daily Mirror

At the day and time appointed for solemnization of Matrimony, the persons to be married shall come into the Marriage Centre with their friends and neighbours (and with an official from the

Department of Fair Trading should they wish to have the marriage contract explained), and there standing together, the Man on the right hand, the Woman on the left, and the Representative of the Department of Marriage in the Middle, the Minister shall say:

Dearly beloved, we are gathered together here in the sight of God, and in the face of this Congregation, and by the authority of the Secretary of State for Marriage, to join together this man and this woman in Holy Matrimony; which is an honourable estate, and which statistics show has risen from 52 per cent of the population in 1939 to 59.3 per cent in 1975 (latest available figures); and is commended of Saint Paul and The White Paper with Green Edges On a Caring Society (HMSO, Cmd 9076); and therefore is not by any to be enterprised, nor taken in hand, unadvisedly, lightly, or wantonly, to satisfy men's carnal lusts and appetites like brute beasts that have no understanding, or in ignorance of the advice freely available at Post Offices, Citizens' Advice Bureaux and Marriage Centres.

First, it was ordained for the procreation of children, to be brought up in the fear and nurture of the Lord, and to be given a fair start in life instead of being thrown on the scrap-heap at school-leaveth age.

Secondly, it was ordained for a remedy against sin, and to avoid fornication, and to reduce the appalling crime and vandalism statistics in the inner cities.

Thirdly, it was ordained for the mutual society, help, and comfort, that the one ought to have of the other, and which is all fully explained in the free booklet, *What Marriage Can Do For You*. Therefore if any man can show any just cause, why they may not lawfully be joined together, let him now make application unto an Unfair Marriages Tribunal, or after a period of 60 (sixty) days shall have elapsed, let him for ever hold his peace.

And also, speaking unto the persons that shall be married, he shall say:

You know, I believe it was a very famous statesman who once said, 'I have always thought that every woman should marry, and no man.' But you know, it's no longer a joke when that situation imagined by Benjamin Disraeli is fast becoming reality. Ask Britain's 750,000 one-parent families if they can see anything to laugh about. It's not funny when one partner welshes on the marriage contract – any more than it would be if your local hardware store refused to replace a faulty electric kettle.

As consumers of goods and services we are now protected all the way down the line. Doesn't it make sense that as consumers of happiness and joy we should be similarly protected?

That's why this Government – any Government – must care about caring. Why £100,000,000 is being pumped into its declared policy of making marriages work. Plus special grants for black-spot regions where the high divorce rate is unacceptable.

And you know, this isn't just using tax payers' money to prop up marital lame ducks. It's an investment in our future – your future. Every husband who packs his bags after a quarrel with the little woman makes extra demands on our limited housing stock. And surveys show that domestic rows can affect productivity, cause accidents, encourage drunkenness, and add to the burden of our already overstretched National Health Service. That's why it was the Government's duty to step in. Think about it. All rise.

If there be no impediment lodged in writing before the Unfair Marriage Tribunal, then shall the Minister say unto the Man:

Hast thou (full name and permanent address), been given a copy of the revised edition of the pamphlet, Your Marriage Rights, and hast thou read that pamphlet?

The man shall answer:
I have.

Then shall the Minister say unto the Woman:
Art thou aware of the various benefits to which ye may be entitled, namely thy Wedding Grant, thy Honeymoon Allowance, the topping-up of thy Bottom Drawer Fund to a sum not exceeding fifty per cent of that Fund, thy free Wedding Ring, thy Married Women's Income Tax dispensation, and thy right of access to a Marriage Guidance Counsellor at any reasonable hour?

The Woman shall answer:
I am. (*If the answer shall be,* I am not, *then shall this Solemnization of Matrimony be brought to an halt pending an court of enquiry.*)

Then shall the Minister lead the persons that shall be married to an Desk, where he shall cause to be put before them an Declaration (Form No. M808/76521-94b) which in its salient parts readeth:
Wilt thou (*full name in block capitals*) have this man/ woman (*strike out that which is not applicable*) to thy wedded husband/wife, to live together after God's ordinance in the holy estate of Matrimony and in accordance with the provision of the Marriage Act 1978 and amending legislation? Wilt thou love him/ her, comfort him/her, honour, and keep him/her (obey him, in the case of females only), in sickness and in health; and, forsaking all other, keep thee only unto him/her, so long as ye both shall live? All questions must be answered. The penalties for a false declaration may be severe.

Three copies of the Declaration having been signed, and an Polaroid Wedding Photograph countersigned by an Person of repute such as an Doctor, Solicitor or Clergyman having been

48

affixed unto the top copy, then shall the Minister say:
Who giveth this woman to be married to this man?

The Representative of the Department of Marriage shall say:
I do, as the qualified representative of the Secretary of State for Marriage, under the provisions of the Marriage Act 1978.

Then shall they give their troth to each other in this manner. The Representative, taking them into an Office, shall warn them solemnly of their responsibilities to one another in Marriage; of their duty to care in an caring society; of the importance that the nuclear family hath to the Economy; of the need to cut their Coats according to their Cloth, that the Prices and Incomes Policy be not threatened by their profligacy; and divers matters. Then shall they complete the Marriage Contract in this manner:
I (full name, permanent address, profession or occupation) take thee (full name, permanent address, profession or occupation) to my wedded wife/husband, and undertake as followeth (tick boxes):
☐ To have and to hold from this day forward
☐ For better
☐ For worse
☐ For richer
☐ For poorer
☐ In sickness and/or health
☐ To love and/or to cherish
☐ Till death us do part
NB These offers not valid if contract exchanged on a doorstep. Signatories must be allowed seven days to change their minds.

Their troth having been plighted, then shall the Man and the Woman go back before the Minister, who shall say:
I now pronounce thee man and wife. Those whom the Marriage Act 1978 hath joined together let no man put asunder, on penalty of two years' imprisonment or a maximum fine of £1000 or both.

49

Flag of Inconvenience

Cunard is attempting to transfer cruise liners to foreign flags of convenience, enabling it to hire cheaper foreign crews.

Guardian

Number One Boy Him Log. Day One.

This plenty big day for me-fella. This most plenty big day since the me-fella come belong big-boat-him-have-many-chimney as assistant head steward in the Louis XIV Starlight Grill Room on top deck below more top deck, plenty-big-swank passengers only.

Big-fella-strong-with-scrambled egg-on-cap, him call me-fella up to him stateroom. Him say:

Ah, there you are, Louis XIV Starlight Grill Room Number Two Boy. How you-fella get on along big boat him ride big waves?

Me-fella say: OK, Boss.

Big-fella-strong him say: Mister First Officer Boss been keep beady eye on you, Number Two Boy, and him say you good boy. How you like be Number One Boy? Job pay plenty glass beads enough along more than coolie minimum. You better take damn job chop-chop.

Me-fella say: Boss, what happen to Number One Boy, him plenty belong-nice to plenty-big-swank passengers, him cook them kai-kai along them table, him add Worcester sauce, double cream and Rémy Martin firewater, then light him match and make him go up like him volcano?

Big-fella-strong him say: Him-fella have no more idea of how to flambé a Steak Diane than him back-behind of me-fella sit-upon. Him damn near set Louis XIV Starlight Grill Room on fire today some time after big ball come up in sky. Plenty-big-swank passenger Mr McGregor him had to come down along below sick-bay with singed eyebrows, and plenty-big-swank passenger McGregor him woman, Mrs

McGregor, she-him have hysterics. Him come too big for him boots, that him trouble.

Me-fella say: Me-fella find plenty-big-swank passenger Boss McGregor him woman more small boot narrow fitting, PDQ.

Big-fella-strong him say: Not plenty-big-swank passenger Mr McGregor him woman, you bloody fool Number Two Boy, it Number One Boy who come too big for him boots.

Me-fella say: Boss, Number One Boy him no wear boots. Number One Boy him wearing evening-dress loincloth and black tie.

Big-fella-strong him say: Not any more him doesn't. Evening-dress loincloth and black tie is Number One Boy uniform and Number One Boy him not bloody Number One Boy much damn more along today after them Louis XIV Starlight Grill Room second sitting run all about them lifeboats chop-chop shouting, 'Fire, fire!' Now do you want Number One Boy job, Number Two Boy, or not?

So me-fella are come be Maître d'belong Louis XIV Starlight Grill Room.

Number One Boy Him Log. Day Two.
Me-fella look in glass-it-look-back. Me-fella pretty damn tip-top smart in velveteen loincloth with blue silk cumberbund. Me-fella boss boy now. Me-fella call all together them no-good serve-hot-roll-with-tongs-and-fold-pink-napkin-in-shape-of-swan boys belong Louis XIV Starlight Grill Room, and tell all them we turn over new broom PDQ chop-chop bloody now. That mean no more become legless on silver polish long before big ball in sky him sink in water and last plenty-big-swank passenger him have coffee along enough him after-dinner mints.

Them no-good serving-boys mutter rhubarb-rhubarb but them speak no bad pidgin agin me-fella.

By-m-by, plenty-big-swank passenger Yankee Boss

Mister Zmansky, him-fella come sit in Crow's-nest Bar belong Louis XIV Starlight Grill Room. Him-fella order him drink from Wine Boy and eat plenty cheese footballs. When by-m-by him drink come on silver salver balanced on Wine Boy him head, him-fella clap him hands and call out to me-fella: Sir, would you step over here a moment?

Me-fella say: Yes sir, Mr Yankee Boss Zmansky, sir?

Him-fella point at drink on silver salver balanced on Wine Boy him head and say: Would you call that a very dry martini on the rocks with a twist of lemon?

Me-fella look at drink on silver salver on Wine Boy him head and say: No sir, Mr Yankee Boss Zmansky, sir. Him tube of lighter fuel.

Him-fella say: OK. Now will you tell me what I have to do to get a dry martini around here?

Me-fella say: Sir, Mr Big-fella Belong Papa-him-on-top's Own Country must tell stupid Wine Boy, fetch plenty juniper berry juice with him dash of vermouth clink-clink and him twist of yellow fruit fall from tree pretty damn quick, shaken not stirred. Otherwise stupid Wine Boy fetch glass of pink paraffin with him olive.

Wine Boy hit me-fella on head with him silver salver and say: Me-fella not stupid. Him-fella Mr Big Yankee Boss Zmansky give me-fella plenty big tip so me-fella fetch him-fella Ronsonol from no-good serving boys them personal cellar.

Mr Yankee Boss Zmansky him say: Jesus!

Number One Boy Him Log. Day Two and One More Day.

Me-fella bow-and-scrape to plenty-big-swank-passengers them come for first when-big-ball-in-sky-all-above sitting. Plenty-big-toff passenger Sir Ffitch-Ffrench, him bang him table with him spoon and tell me-fella to get across along-him-fella and him-fella woman with belong-what-name list of kai-kai.

Him-fella point at belong-what-name list under Volaille and say: Head Waiter, is this Coq au vin à la bourguignonne fresh or frozen?

Me-fella say: Sir Boss Mister Big-shot Ffitch-Ffrench, until soon before Number One Boy him get chop, all bird-from-sky on belong-what-name list come from freezer. Him bad man, Lord Boss Mister Ffitch-Ffrench sir. Him get drunk on Brasso and come too big for him boots.

Him-fella say: Never mind all that, Head Waiter. My wife merely wishes to know if the chicken is fresh?

Me-fella say: Sir Mrs Boss Ffitch-Ffrench him woman, all bird-from-sky on belong-what-name list him now so fresh that him not dead yet. Cookie come along from down galley and cut bird-from-sky's throat at plenty-big-swank passengers them table, then him-fella pluck him bird-from-sky feathers while me-fella simmer mushrooms and baby onions in red jump-on-grape water and bird-from-sky blood. Served with fried croutons and a selection of today's freshly-prepared vegetables from him trolley.

Mrs Sir Ffitch-Ffrench him woman say: How absolutely revolting. We shall have the Châteaubriand.

Me-fella say: Yes sir, madam, how you like him cook?

Him woman say: Rare.

Me-fella tell no-good serving boy go down below among galley and tell Cookie him cook Châteaubriand not plenty much for bigshot passenger and him woman chop-chop PDQ. By-m-by him-fella come back with big silver dish-belong-keep-hot.

Me-fella take off him lid and show Châteaubriand to Sir Boss Ffitch-Ffrench and him woman. Him woman say: Aaaarrrrrgggghhhh! It's a raw pig! Oh my God, I'm going to faint!

Me-fella say to no-good serving boy: You-fella bad no-good serving boy, you-fella been at him surgical spirit.

No-good serving boy him say: Me-fella sober as him - wear - wig - and - say - them - jury - have - rightly-found-you-fella-guilty. Cookie him run out of Châteaubṣiand, so him-fella think Sir Mighty Boss Ffitch-Ffrench and him woman them like Cochon de la Saint-Fortunat, done not plenty much chop-chop.

Me-fella say: Him-fella bad Cookie.

By-m-by him-fella Cookie come along up from down below into Louis XIV Starlight Grill Room and try to kill me-fella with him meat-axe.

Number One Boy Him Log. Day Two And Two More Day.
All no-good serving boys drunk on plenty dry martinis with him twist of lemon. Me-fella serve all kai-kai to all plenty-big-swank passengers.

Me-fella run off him feet.

When him-fella eat him main course, by-m-by Mr Yankee Boss Zmansky clap him hands and tell me-fella what him-fella want for him pudding.

Something snap.

Me-fella pick up steak-knife from Table 43 and hold him at Yankee Boss Mister Zmansky him throat. Me-fella say: You bad man, Mr Boss sir! You-fella cannibal! You-fella eat d'agneau aux primeurs with all them trimmings and now you-fella want me-fella kill Lascar deckhand and boil him in pot. You cruel Mister Zmansky sir!

Him-fella shout: What's gotten into you? All I asked for was a goddam Baked Alaska! OK fella, him-fella continue, I've had enough of this, I'm going straight to the captain.

Number One Boy Him Log. No More Day.
Big-fella-strong-with-scrambled-egg-on-cap, him give
me-fella new job swab him deck. Big-fella-strong him
plenty kind man, him-fella not make me-fella take him
job. Him-fella say me-fella can take him or leave him.

Alcoholics Synonymous

A 'sensible drinking' campaign is to be launched by the Health
Department in an attempt to stem the growth of alcoholism.
Daily Telegraph

It's so silly it's worth quoting at length, if only I hadn't
lost it. When I say lost, I don't mean mislaid. I know
exactly where I put it, my memory being as clear as a
what's the word I'm looking for, the thing you ring
with? Button. As clear as a button. Not button, bell.

What was I talking about? Something to do with horse-racing. Grand National. National Front. Front Parlour. Cottage piano.

Got it. *You* were trying to remember the words of 'Father, dear Father, come home with me now,' and *he* was saying if God was impotent, what would happen if you asked Him to create a rock so heavy that not even He could move it, right? I didn't say impotent, I said impertinent. Omnipotent. Then you started crying because everybody hates you, and *I* said—

I *know* what I said, thank you very much. You're a very nice bloke and my oldest friend but one of these days I'm going to smash you right in the teeth. You have a very nasty habit of interrupting people, do you know that? No wonder everybody hates you.

What *I* said was, has anyone seen that advertisement in the thingy about no smoking. As you were. What's his name – Michael Foot. Ministry of Aviation Fuel. Health. They've started this campaign to stop people drinking. Well, not stop. Drink less. Sensible drinking campaign, that was it.

It was so funny I cut it out, but I've lost it. When I say lost, I don't mean mislaid. I know exactly where I put it, my memory being as clear as a brush.

I'm quite aware I'm repeating myself. I'm repeating myself for the very reason that you're not bloody listening. And incidentally, it's Father dear Father, come home with me now, the clock on the thingy strikes ten. Not twelve, ten. So don't talk to me about bloody impaired memory cells.

I cut this piece out and put it in the pillow, right? Because I put it in the pillow, that's why. I put it in the pillow because I put it in the pillow, why does there have to be a reason for everything?

So naturally, when the bed caught fire, this Michael Foot thing went with it. Gazump. Just like that. Tommy Cooper. Not gazump, that's what estate agents do. Whoof. It went up whoof.

I wish it hadn't gone up whoof because it was so funny. Government warning: this double brandy may damage your health. Absolute cockypop. Signed: Michael Foot.

I keep saying Michael Foot, it wasn't Michael Foot at all. It was what's that bloody Japanese paper-tearing game? Orinoko. Mikado. It wasn't him either. Ennals.

I wish I had it with me but the bed caught fire. Did I tell you about the bed catching fire? Christ. Whoof.

What was the figure he quoted now? No, I know you don't know, it's a rotundal question. I'm going to tell you, aren't I? Eleven out of something, that was it. Eleven out of something people have a serious drink problem. Codswallow.

I don't have a serious drink problem. Do you have a serious drink problem? Does *he* have a serious drink problem? So that's four of us without a serious drink problem – and you've got to bear in mind that we're pissed. Add up all the people who aren't pissed and how do they get the figure of eleven out of something?

Do you know why I drink? Shall I tell you why I drink? Shall I tell you why I drink? Shall I tell you why I drink? Shall I tell you why I drink? Shall I tell you why I drink? Shall I tell you why I drink? Shall I tell you why I drink?

I don't give a sod why *you* drink, I'm telling you why *I* drink. Do you want to know why I drink or do you want this glass rammed down your throat?

I drink to be sociable.

I do, I drink to be sociable. Whatever Michael Foot may say, he's talking pure codswallow. I do not have a drinking problem. No, I know you don't, that's what I'm saying if you'll just wash your bloody ears out and listen, we drink to be sociable. We could give it up tomorrow. Last week. For a fortnight.

All right, so I like a drink in the morning, that's supposed to be the first sign. There's one simple drink why I have a reason in the morning and that's to get through the day's work. You have to drink in my kind of work, it's compulsory. Not compulsory, thingy. What's the word where it means you're driven to it? Golf. Parsnip. Compulsive. Because of the pressure. You *have* to drink, otherwise you'd go stark staring sober. But I'm telling you, sonny boy, I can do my job on my head. In fact, I often *have* done it on my head.

Then there's drinking at lunch-time. To hear Origami talk, if you have a drink at lunch-time you're well on the way to being a necrophiliac. That might be so if you *have* to drink at lunch-time. I don't *have* to drink at lunch-time, I *do* drink at lunch-time. That's a very very very very very very very very different kettle of ballgame altogether.

I drink at lunch-time for one reason and one lunch-time only. Because I'm happy. I am. Put me in that pub at lunch-time and I'm as happy as a Chinaman. And I'll tell you something else if you promise to get it let no further. *You'd* drink at lunch-time if you were married to that cow Noreen.

Yes, I realize you *are* married to that cow Noreen, but only in a sense. Only in a sense. Only in a sense. You see, words are very strange things, they have different meanings, I've studied this a lot. So when I say that cow Noreen, yes, granted, agreed, she is quite rightly married to you. I mean, you could divorce her tomorrow and she'd still be your wife. But. But. But. You're not having it off with her, and I am.

That's certainly not what she told me, my friend. According to her, you've been omnipotent for years. That just shows you what a cow she is. And then Michael Ennals wonders why I've got to have a drink at lunch-time.

Aren't you going to knock me down, then? Aren't you going to ask me to step outside? I believe that's the usual form in these circumstances. After all, I did knock *you* down when you told me you were having it off with *my* wife, didn't I? I know I did. And she's an even bigger cow than Noreen.

That's what I like about you, you're mature. You are. I've never said this to you before, and I wouldn't say it now if I hadn't had a few, but you are the most mature man I've every known. I mean, I'm not mature, but you are mature. Yes you are, you're mature. And another thing, you're yellow.

Come outside then.

Just a minute, while I'm taking my jacket off, I've got a very funny newspaper cutting to show you in my inside pocket.

The bloody thing should be here somewhere. It's about this new sensible swimming campaign, sensible drinking campaign, did you read about it? How drinking's supposed to make you aggressive, maudlin, inefficient, immoral and Christ knows what else besides. And what else does it do? Oh, yes, it makes you lose your thingy. Begins with a D. Memory.

I definitely had it when we were asked to leave those pubs. No, I didn't, I remember now. I put it in the thingy. Jigsaw. Salt-spoon. Funicular railway. Before I set the bed on fire.

Did I have a lighted pillow with me when we got out of that taxi?

Dave Copperfield

Chap IV. I Am Taken Into Care

On the last night of my restraint, I was awakened by hearing my own name spoken in a whisper. I started up in bed, and putting out my arms in the dark said:

'Is that you, Peggotty?'

There was no immediate answer, but presently I heard my name again, or what I took to be my name, for it was a diminutive I had never heard from Peggotty's lips nor any other's.

I groped my way to the door, and putting my face to the key hole, whispered:

'But why do you call me "Dave", Peggotty dear?'

The strangest of voices, at once educated and coarse, whispered back. 'No hassle, Dave, it's the social workers. Hang about, we're just getting the lock open with a 'airpin.'

After some scratching, and damning, and blasting, and 'S–dit' and 'Sssh!', the door at long last gave way, and I beheld upon the threshold two apparitions, so alike that they might be twins, and clad from head to toe in faded denim. Then I saw that the hair about their faces was in the case of one of them an unkempt beard, so confirming his masculinity. The sex of his companion, a person like himself of some twenty-three summers, was vouchsafed to me only by the production, from a commodius ethnic shoulder-bag, of a piece of paste-board, covered in plastic, introducing her as a Miss Grimdrag, from the Council.

Meantime her colleague's own visiting card, fished out of a ragged top pocket from which Disque Bleu cigarettes spilled in profusion, announced him as a Mr Jollyup, of the same address, and at my service.

Miss Grimdrag and Mr Jollyup – as I still thought of my new friends, for try as I may I could not bring myself to call them Viv and Kev, as the latter had suggested – seated themselves on my bed, and counselled me, speaking in turns, to remain cool and to let it all hang out, while for their part they proposed to get it all together.

'Ve've been getting feedback on you from the neighbours,' Miss Grimdrag informed me, producing a fat spiral notebook and ballpoint pen from her many-coloured bazaar-on-a-strap. 'Just give us your case history, Dave, vould you?'

'To begin my life with the beginning of my life,' I ventured, 'I record that I was born (as I have been informed and believe) on a Friday, at twelve o'clock at night. It was remarked that the clock began to strike—'

'Like, briefly,' interjected Mr Jollyup.

'Briefly, sir, my dear Mama, my father's eyes having closed upon the light of the world six months before mine opened upon it, took the name of Mr Murdstone who thereupon beat me up and has kept me locked in my room these five days. The length of those five days I can convey no idea of to anyone. They occupy the place of years in my remembrance . . .'

'Found-in-traumatic-state,' murmured Mr Jollyup, as if dictating to Miss Grimdrag who was scribbling in her notebook. Of myself he asked: 'Vy did the bastard beat you up, Dave? Caught you playing with yourself, that type of perfectly naturally behaviour in a boy of your age?'

61

'I could not learn my lessons, sir.'

'Lessons, Dave? Sex lessons, vould they be? Did he ask you to pose for wicious photographs, anything of that kind?'

'Worse than that, sir. They were appalling sums, invented for me, and delivered to me orally by Mr Murdstone. "If I go into a cheesemonger's shop, and buy five thousand double-Gloucester cheeses at four-pence-halfpenny each, present payment." That sort of thing, sir. Except that on the day he beat me up, he made it five thousand canes.'

'Canes,' repeated Mr Jollyup, grimacing fiercely at Miss Grimdrag. 'Did he ever ask you to whip him, Dave?'

'O, never, sir, upon my honour!'

'Did he show you any books, love?' Miss Grimdrag then asked, as if it should be the most innocent question in the world (and might have been for aught I knew, but for a further exchange of most ferocious glances between my interrogators).

'If you please, miss, only my school books.'

'The ones he finds these four-and-a-half-pee cheeses in?' And to Mr Jollyup, rather than to myself, Miss Grimdrag added with a sneer: 'What century did *he* do his teacher-training in?'

'Right!'

Miss Grimdrag scrawled in her notebook so viciously that the ballpoint all but tore the page. Fearful that I might be called to task for giving a false account of my stepfather I blurted out: 'But Miss Grimdrag! Mr Jollyup! Mr Murdstone is not a teacher, he is a wine merchant!'

'O, unqualified, is he? Christ, Viv, we've nailed the s–d!' Thus, in tones of great triumph, Mr Jollyup to Miss Grimdrag. To which the latter responded: 'Right! He couldn't be in a more culpable child-custody situation if he'd gone for the boy with a red-hot poker. Don't vorry, Dave, ve'll have you in council care before nightfall.'

'You'll like the hostel accommodation, Dave,' encouraged Mr Jollyup, as if in answer to my unspoken reservations. 'You'll be in a one-to-one relationship with people your own age-group. Vhere was that place we put young Nick Nickleby, Viv – think Dave would like that?'

'Dotheboys Hall? I believe it's subject to an official inquiry just at the moment, Kev – there's been some unfounded allegations against the house warden. I thought ve might try a referral to Salem House.'

I venture to confess that a sob then escaped my lips, at the prospect of parting from my dear Mama and that kind soul, Peggotty. Mr Jollyup must have noticed my distress, for with manly gruffness he changed the subject of conversation.

'Just one or two more questions for the record, Dave. This Faggotty you thought vas coming in ven Viv and me broke the door down – has he ever interfered with you?'

'Begging your pardon, sir, you must be referring to Peggotty, my nurse. Allow me to say, Mr Jollyup, sir, with all the force at my command, that a gentler, more honest creature . . .'

'A *nurse*? At your age?'

Mr Jollyup would have continued, but again I comprehended a mute signal from Miss Grimdrag, to which he responded by closing one eye and tapping his nose with the forefinger of the right hand. It occurred to me, that my two friends must know one another very well, that they were able to communicate in the language of winks and nods.

'Does this Peggotty still bath you, Dave?' asked Miss Grimdrag, as casually and airily as she might have asked, 'Does this Peggotty still wear a mob-cap?' or 'Does this Peggotty still bring your supper on a tray?'

'Most certainly she does not, Miss Grimdrag,' said I, and I make no doubt that my cheeks were flaming. 'I am of an age to bath myself, and in any case Miss

Murdstone would never allow it.'

'Yeah, I vas going to ask you about Miss Murdstone,' said Mr Jollyup. 'Ve have a report that generally speaking she don't like boys. Has she ever strung you up by the ankles, Dave, or anything similar.'

'Miss Murdstone, sir, is my jailer, appointed so by her brother,' I reported. 'It is thanks to Miss Murdstone that these five days are so vividly and strongly stamped on my remembrance. The depressed dreams and nightmares I have had – the return of day, noon, afternoon, evening, when the boys played in the churchyard, and I watched them from a distance within this room, being ashamed to show myself at the window lest they should know I was a prisoner – the strange sensation of never hearing myself speak – the setting in of rain one evening, with a fresh smell, and its coming down faster and faster between me and the church, until it and gathering night seemed to quench me in gloom, and fear, and remorse . . .'

'Better leave it, Kev, he's clamming up,' said Miss Grimdrag with yet another of her meaningful glances, at the same time making a great performance of closing her notebook.

Mr Jollyup then – responding as an actor might to his cue – smote me heartily upon the shoulder blades, and lit a cigarette with a great air of nonchalance.

'Anyway, it's all over now, Dave. The Law might come round to Salem House to take a statement, but that's no big hassle.'

'O, sir!' Another sob shuddered through my frame. 'What is to become of me?'

'Cool it, Dave. You'll stay in care till you've taken your "O" levels, then ve'll find you a job.'

'There's a werry nice varehouse down Blackfriars. They sometimes take on youths under the Job Creation Scheme,' said Miss Grimdrag, gathering up her things. 'Now blow your nose, Dave, and say goodbye to your mum.'

A child of excellent abilities, yet soon hurt bodily and mentally, it had ever seemed wonderful to me that nobody should have made any sign in my behalf. But now, at long last, a caring society was taking me to its bosom.

Next week: Chap V. My papers are mixed up with Oliver Twist's and there is a committee of inquiry at the Workhouse.

The Least Influential Hundred

In New York, where current literature has been reduced to lists of names and dates, one of the Top Ten dinner-party games is derived from a best-seller called *The 100*.

The 100 is a list of the hundred most influential people who ever lived, beginning with Muhammed, Isaac Newton and Jesus Christ and ending with Neils Bohr of atomic structure fame. The object of the game is to argue as loudly as possible about whether the author has got his list in the right order, whether he should have included John F. Kennedy when Abraham Lincoln does not get a look in, and similar variations on historic name-dropping.

On this side of the Atlantic *The 100* game will probably catch on in Hampstead, but elsewhere its appeal will be minimal. With our great mistrust of professional achievement, we are more interested in the unsuccessful than the successful.

Accordingly, in order to adapt the game to British tastes, I have drawn up a list of the hundred least influential people who ever lived. The guideline I have followed – so as to exclude such as Mr Percy Throstle, of Redroofs, Sycamore Avenue, West Wycombe, an insurance assessor of such insignificance and lack of character that neighbours continue to send him Christmas cards four years after his death – is that only persons of some unique achievement, however minuscule, may qualify.

Sidney Epps Inventor of several Esperanto dialects, notably Eebahgoombo (West Yorkshire Universal Language). Expelled from the movement after the backslang controversy of 1920.

Lionel Shallows Schoolmaster. Tired of scraping his knuckles on the blackboard, Shallows developed a chalk-holder made of tin, somewhat on the lines of a propelling pencil. The invention is said to have fallen out of use when it was trodden on by a milk monitor.

Edmund Gant Sociologist. Discovered that of 614 manual workers living in or around Wolverhampton, 493 'liked a drink', 85 'sometimes liked a drink' and the remainder drank 'only at Christmas style of thing' or not at all.

R. P. Transom VAT Administrator. Proposed that untreated camel fat, when imported by manufacturers of surgical liniment or painters' sundrymen (but not dog-boarding kennels), should be zero-rated.

K. L. Wemyss Traffic engineeer. Painted experimental double yellow lines along a section of railway track near Swindon.

Friedrich Strauss The fourth son of the eminent Austrian composer, he could see no future in the waltz and spent a lot of time trying to popularize the four-step, later becoming a successful clerk.

Elmer Wyatt Remington Press Secretary and publicity manager of James K. Polk, 11th President of the United States. His designs for a Polk Memorial are believed to be somewhere in the Smithsonian Institute.

Maurice Shallows Brother of Lionel Shallows (qv), inventor of the blackboard chalk-holder. Maurice claimed to the last that the idea was his.

Elspeth N. Hetherington Author of *A life: Some Accounts of A Lady, Who, Having Regard To That Station To Which She was Called, Stayed At Home Jam-Bottling During The Crimean War*. In three volumes.

Herbet Knell Discovered that drinking a glass of water from the wrong side can cause hiccups, as well as curing them.

Chung Ki Ling By tying firecrackers to the tail of a kite, developed the exploding kite which had a brief vogue during the T'Ang dynasty.

Samuel Eckersley Author of Eckersley's formula: that, a bus of a certain route-number not having reached a specified request stop within a period of half an hour, four will then come at once.

John Batts-Wycherman Sometime Member of Parliament who, in 1936, asked the Prime Minister if he had any plans to visit South Ealing. When the Premier replied: 'Yes, sir, I am going there this afternoon,' all the tongue-tied MP could think of to say was, 'Good.' The Speaker ruled that this was not a supplementary question.

Alphonse Duval Waiter. Found that by placing a folded-up piece of cardboard under the leg of a table, he could stop it from rocking about when diners cut into their meat. Escoffier, however, said that the ruse was common long before Duval arrived on the scene.

Theobald Jones A friend of one of the hundred most influential persons in history, namely Adam Smith, who popularized economics as a science. Used to discourage Smith by saying, 'Yes, I understand what you mean by wealth but the rest of it goes over my head, I'm afraid.'

John the Netmaker Reputedly the discoverer of the Isle of Man while out fishing. Other sources say that the island had been very well known for many centuries, and that it was not worth discovering anyway.

Douglas Purdie Amateur poet. According to Inland Revenue files, if not the first man to write a letter of complaint to his tax inspector in rhyming couplets, then certainly the first one to get a reply likewise in verse.

Karl Schumacher Part-time scientist. Several times successfully induced splitting headaches in a domestic cat, but abandoned his experiments when asked by his children what he thought he was proving.

V. L. Boronov Dramatist. Argued passionately for 'time-realism' in the theatre – in other words, a play should last as long as the events it describes. After attempting an adaptation of *War and Peace*, was urged by Chekhov to get into some other line of work.

Charles Godfrey Carpenter County planning officer. Ruled that a 'No Hawkers' sign on the gate of a semi-detached house was an illegal advertisement hoarding, and fought the case all the way to the House of Lords.

The Rev. Septimus Oates   Sometime curate of Weston Longueville Church, Norfolk, and later visiting chaplain to Marie Antoinette during the French Revolution, was advised by Parson Woodforde to keep a diary. Didn't.

Evangeline Shallows   Sister of Lionel and Maurice Shallows (qv) who late in life said that neither of her brothers had made a blackboard chalk-holder out of tin, it was just something that Lionel used to talk about from time to time.

M. Tulse   Botanist. Although undistinguished in this field, he was well-known in the Theydon Bois area for his imitation of an angry swan.

George W. Remington   Son of Elmer Wyatt Remington (qv) and a distant connection of the typewriter family, he claimed to have discovered that a straightened-out paper-clip is the best thing for cleaning the letter 'o'. This is disputed (the claim, not the discovery).

Llewellyn Ap Evans   A film documentary writer living in Frith Street during the nineteen-forties, he says that although he once saw Dylan Thomas going into a shop, he never actually met him.

It will be observed – particularly by R. Noakes, who, as the writer of a letter to the Carlsberg Brewery suggesting bottled lager-and-lime, was No 26 on the list – that only twenty-five of the One Hundred Least Influential People in History are mentioned here. The other seventy-five are also-rans.

Scanning Permission

Notes on the need for planning permission under the Town and Country Planning Act (Spring Development Order) as amended 1983.

Definition

In the northern hemisphere, Spring is that season which extends, or could extend, from the vernal equinox to the summer solstice. More precisely, it has been suggested (*Old Moore v Secretary of State*) that Spring commences on or around March 21 when the Sun enters the sign Aries. This, however, is an astronomical and not a statutory definition, though some limited public access to this date may now exist as of usage.

Planning

Under the Act, the Spring and its associated activities may be (but not necessarily are: see under *Uses*) subject to the same planning regulations and restrictions as may from time to time be applied to any other undertaking such as a smelting works or mineral quarry.

The purpose of planning is to harmonize the environment and enforce standards, and to protect the public against undesirable developments such as a linseed boiling plant or animal charcoal manufactory in a residential zone, or darling buds of May in late June.

In general, neither construction work on the Spring nor capital outlay on any Springlike activity should be commenced or contracted for until outline permission has been received from the local authority. Application may be made on forms obtainable from the Department of the Environment, and must be in verse.

Uses

Among the legitimate uses of Spring are and have

been held to be at various times, gambolling, billing, cooing, blooming, blossoming, cleaning, bonnet-wearing, hey-ding-a-dinging, tiptoeing through tulips, wandering lonely as clouds, and becoming feverish. Where such uses are or have been or could be constant, ie and eg, where it can be demonstrated that the joys of Spring are not materially different from the joys of Winter, Autumn and/or Summer (but preferably all three), then planning permission would not normally be required. But it was held (*Locksley Parish Council v Tennyson*) that in Spring a young man's fancy lightly turning to thoughts of love was *change of use*, in that he had previously been thinking about something else, so an application for planning permission should have been made. A blithe spirit, however, (*Department of Health and Social Security v Shelley*) wert never a bird and so no change of use was entailed when it was hailed in an ode.

Development
Planning permission must always be obtained where development is anticipated. *Development*, as defined in Schedule 1 of the Act, means a substantial alteration to the environment such as the building of any light railway, the formation of fattening units for pigs on non-agricultural land, or the construction of any Spring wedding. It is not the same as *Improvement* (see below), such as any concrete base for swillbins where the fattening units already exist, or any proposal of marriage where the lady is already pregnant.

Within this definition, all Spring developments are deemed to be subject to the general provisions of the Act. Thus the loveliest of trees, the cherry now, when it is hung with bloom along the bough and stands about the woodland ride wearing white for Eastertide, is (*see Salop County Council v Housman*) subject to the same Use Classes Order as a commercial training college, vehicle storage depot or shop for the sale of hot food.

Gambolling when carried out by lambs is the same as silt-dredging. A cuckoo's nest is a hutment or shed, but not a caravan; while a lovenest, if intended for human habitation, is an aerodrome and therefore subject to a public inquiry and a report from an inspector appointed by the Minister before permission to operate it may be granted. Spring fever is deemed to be the same as swine fever, and may result in sufferers being served an Order requiring them not to carry out their activities near any school building nor within 25 metres of the metalled portion of a classified road.

It has been submitted (*Meteorological Office v Shelley*) that Winter is a development under the Act, since it was evident from its arrival that Spring could not be far behind. But where some hounds of Spring were on Winter's traces (*Our Dumb Friends' League v Swinburne*) this was not accepted as sufficient proof of an unauthorized boarding kennel.

Improvements
Permission is not normally needed for improvements of a nonstructural nature, for instance repainting the white lines on the greyhound racing track or falling in love. Lovemaking (*League of Purity v D. H. Lawrence, on appeal to House of Lords*) is not the same as the placing and storage on land of pipes and other apparatus needed for the installation of a gas distribution system. The Act says, 'If confined to passing o'er green cornfields, lying between acres of the rye and crowning love with the prime in the Springtime (this period to incorporate the only pretty ring time), then any works carried out by any lover upon his lass, whether or not accompanied by a hey and/or a ho and/or a hey nonny no, are not works for making good war damage or to do with drains or public utilities or gravedigging.' Consequently planning permission is not needed, except from the girl's father. But a man who held up traffic to tell a lass

so neat with smile so sweet that she had won his right good will and that he would crowns resign to call her his (*Richmond Borough Council v Oxford Song Book and others*) was committing an offence even though not in breach of the act.

Exemptions

The Crown Agents, county authorities where they are responsible for the construction of and upkeep of carriageways, flood barriers and lunatic asylums, the Ministry of Defence when engaged in certain works, and God while in his heaven, are outside the scope of the Act. This exemption applies also to any works that may be carried out by any servant or agent of the exempted bodies, while performing duties which would be exempt were they to be performed by the exempted bodies. Thus it has been held (*Camden Council v God*) that while the year may be at the Spring, no permission is needed for the hillside to be dew-pearled, the lark to be on the wing or the snail to be on the thorn, always provided that God's in his heaven and assuming sworn affidavits that all's right with the world.

It has been ruled (*GLC v Novello, ex parte Chappel & Co Ltd copyright MCMXLV*) that where a couple gathered some lilacs in the Spring 'again' – in other words for a second or third time – then walked together down an English lane, planning permission was no longer required. They were in the same position as a travelling breeder of maggots from putrescible animal matter who has permission to dispose of small quantities of effluvia in a disused brick kiln. Provided that the limits imposed are not exceeded – not more that one tonne of bone, fat and offal, or one large vaseful of tulips – there is nothing in the planning certificate to say that it is a 'one-off' operation that may not be repeated.

The judgement on the gathering of flowers may also apply to the process of growing them. Thus golden daffodils, always provided they do not exceed a crown or host in quantity, may if not in infringement of local by-laws flutter and dance in the breeze without permission, so long as they do so quietly. But some flowers that bloomed in the Spring, tra la, were held (*Noise Abatement Society v W. S. Gilbert*) to be a nuisance. This ruling has also been applied to some birds that sang, hey ding a ding, ding.

Zoning

The zoning regulations are flexible – eg, the first rustle of Spring is judged to be an ice cream van, so that it may travel anywhere within reason – but this flexibility does not always work on the side of the applicant. The application of a man who wanted to be in England now that April was there was rejected because he could not show cause why he should not spend April in Paris.

Right off their Rockers

Young Conservatives are being urged to adopt a more
political role in an attempt to stem further defections
to the Social Democrats from the party's youth wing.

Observer

'Fiona! As I live and breathe!'

'Nige! How *are* you? It's been yonks!'

'Absolute eras! What have you been up to in fact?'

'In fact I was not a minute ago decanted in Sloane Square by Bruno, having zoomed back from Sussex where a fabulous time was had by all at the rally. We thought we might have seen you there.'

'Couldn't make it, sob sob. *A*, I promised to hold Pru's hand on the People's March Against Ken Livingstone, and *B*, the Land Rover's misbehaving again.'

'Not the *car* rally, idiot! The Support The Neutron Bomb Rally in the paddock at David's papa's place. Literally everybody was there except you and Pru, excuses excuses. Great time. Then we all bombed down to Brighton for the Third World Ball, when enormous quantities of champagne were consumed and Gervaise went for a swim with his things on.'

'Ya, I feel really shitty at missing that gig but there was no way we could make it except by ducking the sit-in outside County Hall, and that wouldn't have been fair on Tara and Dominic who'd spent their entire weekend slaving away at our Bring Back Horace Cutler banners.'

'Poor lambs, and Tara's always been so hopeless at

75

tapestry. Never mind, paps you can make amends by turning out for the Reigate and Banstead Five.'

'I don't believe I'm into the Reigate and Banstead Five. What are they – heavy metal?'

'No ducky, they're Robin, Nicholas, Tessa, Podgy and Caroline. Surely you knew they'd been arrested?'

'I heard they were in trouble with the fuzz sort of, but I gathered Podgy's mama had uttered words in the right ears.'

'My dear, no way could even Podgy's mum get them out of this one. You do realize they were caught red-handed painting "We the undersigned oppose the principle of the closed shop and call upon Government to introduce legislation to preserve the right of the individual to choose whether or not to become a member of a Trade Union" across the entire frontage of Harrods? They're up at Bow Street on Friday as ever was, so we all fully intend boogying along to shout "Free the Reigate and Banstead Five" from the gallery and generally make nuisances of ourselves.'

'Paps I could bring the horn off the Bugatti, and make all sorts of rude noises at the magistrates.'

'Do, oh pretty-please, Nige! And Gervaise swears he means to throw flour bombs at all and sundry, whereupon he's bound to be promptly arrested himself and will be known henceforth as the Belgravia One.'

'Talking of whom, aren't Gervaise and Zoë sponsible for this year's Remember Pol Pot barbecue?'

'Ya. Shall you and Pruzie-poo be among those present?'

'Ya, we thought we might stagger along.'

'Oh, you truly-ruly must, it promises to be a gas. There's to be gingerbread boat-people for pudding and guess what's first prize in the tombola? A really really pretty Vietnamese au pair girl. Kindly donated, as they say, by those celebrated newlyweds Georgina and Simon Cope-Hope-Hetheringthon-Wetherington. Parrently they were given two in their wedding shower.'

'In fact have Georgey and Simon had you round to Walton Street yet?'

'In fact ya. Sweet little doll's house, isn't it? They lent us their drawing-room for a meeting of the Young Conservatives Demand Action Against the Homeless Now Committee.'

'Why are you against the homeless, exactly?'

'Really, Nige, you are thick sometimes! We're not against the homeless, piglet, we're against the homeless not having homes. We're trying to encourage them all to join building societies. Exhausting work but great fun, really really.'

'I spect that's why we never see you at the every-fourth-Saturday Stop Police Harassment dinner-dance these days.'

'That and the fact that if one's been to one Stop Police Harassment dinner-dance one's been to them all, and besides it's not my bag, I prefer disco.'

'But in fact you *are* in favour of stopping the police being harassed?'

'Oh, ya.'

'Then don't you paps think paps you should paps stand up and be counted?'

'Promise not to be cross, Nige, but do you know, Henrietta Shaughan-Vaughan-Bassingham-Massingham was absolutely right – you *do* look like Mr Toad when you're being pompous. Sweet!'

'No, I'm sorry, Fio, but at the risk of being boring boring, this does happen to be deadly serious. One hates to say this, but if you and Jessica and Belinda and the Terrible Twins and the rest of your Young Monetarists crowd turn up your pretty little noses at grassroots participation, then we may as well pack it all in and leave it to the Social Democrats.'

'. . . Said he, giving his well-known imitation of Lord Thorneycroft.'

'You may scoff, darling, but it's woefully true, I promise. Look what happened to the dreaded Labour Party. The moderates were content to sit back and let

77

the Trots organize their dinner-dances and now of course all their garden fêtes, gymkhanas, hunt balls and what-have-you are entirely in the hands of the Far Left.'

'You don't think you're paps being the teeniest-weeniest bit unfair?'

'Very well, if you won't take my word, sulk sulk ask Miles Mayne-Brayne-Coppington-Toppington. His father got it first hand from a great chum of Woy Jenkins no less, name-drop name-drop.'

'One didn't mean unfair on the Far Left, silly billy, one meant unfair on one. After all, who was it passed up a weekend in Scotland in order to crash up to grotty Liverpool for the Right to Work march?'

'Surely that was a socialist thrash?'

'They did have, ya, but theirs was quite a generalized affair. Ours was purely in support of Babs Lancashire's People's Campaign To Import Filipino Houseboys As Cargo.'

'Then all harsh words taken back and apologies are in order. Kiss kiss?'

'I shan't forgive you unless you buy either one of my Wets Out badges or a Honk If You're A Monetarist bumper sticker or preferably both. All proceeds to the League For Cruel Sports.'

'I'll rashly invest in one of each provided you disgorge suitably large sums for one of my Support Education Cuts T-shirts. In aid of TIFF.'

'TIFF being?'

'Tory Teachers In Favour of Flogging. Now I really must fly Fio, I want to get to the Right Wing Bookshop before it closes. Give Bruno all sorts of messages.'

'Oodles of love to Pruzie-poo. You must both come to dinner and resume those lovely gossips we used to have about curing inflation.'

These Foolish Things . . .

Memory Lane, sir? Follow your nose as far as the army badges shop, fork right where you see the stall selling repro tram tickets, keep straight on down the Portobello Road and Memory Lane's on your left, just past the old Welsh Dairy. *My Old Granny's Nightdress* it's called, these days . . .

The glass marbles you stuck up your nostrils as a boy are antiques now. Those enchanting paper dolls your sister used to play with might be up at Christie's next week if only you hadn't chucked them on the fire when she jumped up and down on your Dinky fire engine. Dinky toys, any condition – even, presumably, in the condition of having been jumped up and down on – are desperately sought in the columns of *Exchange and Mart*.

Nostalgia doesn't come cheap any more. Wallowing among the pages of Gamages' catalogue for 1935 (itself, like practically everything else produced in that vintage year, a collector's item) is like browsing through an old bound volume of the *Investors Chronicle*, if only there were such an item on the market these days.

The 'Little Maid' house-cleaning set with brush, pan, feather duster and tiny tin of Mansion Polish mounted on card – our price 2/11 (ah! whatever happened to 2/11?), yours for £10, or £8.50 trade. The

'Joiboy' pull-along wooden horse on wheels, recommended retail price 17/6, call it thirty-five quid if still with the original paint.

Looking back through the veil of tears, how many bags of gold dust did we give away to the jumble sale? How many annuities swopped for an all-day sucker? How many investment portfolios left to rust in the back yard? We must have thrown fortunes away between us.

Or rather, you must: I'm not so sure about myself. My own Memory Lane owing more to Hogarth than Mabel Lucie Atwell (who, by the way, is fetching more than first run engravings of *The Four Stages of Cruelty* these days: snap her up), I have to delve a full arm's-length into the dream cupboard of childhood to come up with anything of value.

What offers for a lead soldier (Britain's series No. 27 Brass Band of the Line, rare), sucked only once? A set of cigarette cards, or meal tickets for life as they are known these days, bearing representations of famous locomotives, only four of them stuck together? An 'Ever-Ready' cycle lamp, hopefully to be attached one day to a 'Raleigh' bicycle, unused except for reading under the bedclothes?

The rest was junk. But that's what they used to say about old teapots in the shape of thatched cottages or famous locomotives, and now Sotheby's are taking bids for the things by satellite. You never know your luck. I can lose nothing by dusting off the playthings of my oft-remembered days of innocence and listing them in my own Bumper Catalogue. All items are as found: no money refunded. Not responsible for marmalade stains.

The 'Hoppity' Series (1). The 'Hoppity' farmyard set. This is a collection of farm animals all with three legs, except for the turkeys, ducks and geese which have one. The 'De Luxe' editon also features a milkmaid with no head and a one-armed farmer. A construction toy, the 'Hoppity' farmyard set includes a kit of bits of matchstick which can be poked into the animals' carcasses to replace the missing limbs.

The 'Hoppity' Series (2). The 'Hoppity' roller skate. This is a single roller skate with three wheels and an ankle strap. The toe clamps are optional to the point of non-existence. Hours of fun can be got from attaching the 'Hoppity' roller skate to either foot and trailing it along the street in search of some surface not covered by lethal gravel chippings.

The 'Rowntree' cocoa tin, A really educational toy. Punch holes in the lid to make a home for caterpillars, or roll it out flat to make a length of tin. By applying the 'Rowntree' cocoa tin over the mouth and sucking in deeply, the effect can be achieved of defying gravity, since it will adhere to the face without visible support.

Rainbow Blob Plasticine. Plasticine, the popular modelling material, is now available in a multi-coloured blob. Predominantly greyish, the blob incorporates streaks of green, blue and sort of orange, which can easily be scraped off and stored under the fingernails during use. Rainbow Blob Plasticine's malleable qualitites make it eminently suitable for stuffing down those metal protection caps that you have on pencils, or forming into lozenges to attach to the sole of the shoe.

The 'Skipper' sardine key. Useful for carrying in the pocket, swallowing, or tying string to. Has a jagged bit of metal on the end which attaches magically to the lower lip.

The 'Bumper' pile of comics. Twelve, yes twelve, assorted comics, all guaranteed different. Each 'Bumper' pile contains a first-day-of-issue *Dandy*, the middle four pages of Radio Fun, a piece of corrugated cardboard, some jam, and a rare comic supplement from a Toronto Sunday newspaper. Fun for all the family. Swop comics with your friends! Stuff them under the sofa cushion! Rescue them from the dustbin! Tell your mother that you are keeping them for a special purpose!

Pocket Meccano. Unlike the conventional Meccano construction outfit with its hundreds of girders, strips and plates, pinions, cranks, wheels, brackets, nuts and bolts, Pocket Meccano does not have to be kept in a big box. Consisting of a single strip of scratched green metal with little holes in it, it can be carried in the top pocket so that everyone will think you have got the rest of the set at home. Pocket Meccano has a thousand uses. Flick paper pellets with it. Hold it up to your eyes and squint through the little holes. Full of excitement with an endless variety of interest. No spare parts to lose. Make carrying Pocket Meccano about with you your hobby at once!

The 'Adana' Printing Machine Advertisement. A genuine advertisement for an 'Adana' printing machine, telling you how you can print anything from chemist's labels to an illustrated magazine for only 57/6, or £2 17s 6d when you have worked out what it really costs. Packed with hundreds of closely-printed words, including exciting phrases such as 'automatic self-inking', 'no special skill required' and 'two-coloured illustrated particulars and samples of work sent on receipt of stamp'. Every 'Adana' Printing Machine Advertisement includes a large two-tone drawing of the actual machine, with little arrows pointing out the platten, inking bed and many other fascinating details. Can be studied for hours. With the aid of this unique Advertisement, pester your parents for an 'Adana' Printing Machine! Hope to get one for Christmas! Work out that it would only take two and a half years' pocket money to buy one yourself! A really absorbing hobby for the Modern Boy.

The 'Scribble-oh' Library. A delightful series of annuals, medical encyclopedias, family Bibles and Thrilling Tales of Adventure at Sea, all hand-illustrated in crayon, indelible pencil, water-colour or pen and ink. Illustrations range from Jackson Pollock-type scribbles on the fly-leaves to illuminated capital letters painstakingly inked-in by hand. Further volumes in preparation.

The 'Junior Pathologist' Dead Mouse. This item has been withdrawn.

Scot Free

A cartoon leaflet was launched yesterday, aimed at discouraging young Scots from seeking the bright lights of London. The leaflet says that if they really must go they should have at least £200 to help them through the first difficult days.

Guardian

From: McTavish, Planning
To: McLavish, Graphics
Subject: Discouraging young Scots from seeking bright lights of London.

While I have nothing but praise for the artwork of your department's cartoon depicting a desolate young Scot sitting, against the background of a hostile-looking Piccadilly Circus, upon a Dick Whittington-type milestone inscribed 'Tae Glasgae, 400 miles' under a symbolic black cloud labelled ' Southern Unfriendliness', I wonder if this would quite get our message across. Given that we are urging these young chaps not to cross the border with less than £200 in their trews, perhaps a completely opposite approach might hit the nail squarely on the head. I append some observations which may inspire your doodling pencil:

Tendency of many London pubs to run to tartan decor as Indian restaurants run to red flock wallpaper. Probability of typical young Scot having been given address of at least one of these establishments before leaving Scotland, with counsel that he has only to mention name Mac to be treated like son of house.

Predisposition of young Scot to aim for recommended pub like thirst-crazed homing pigeon within three minutes of arrival at King's Cross, if only to avoid importunities of fellow-country-men staggering after him along Caledonian Road clutching half-bottles of surgical spirit and addressing him as Jimmy.

Likelihood of pub landlady not remembering Mac by name while being sure of knowing him like own son if he walked through door, also jocularly telling young Scot she bets he's never from north of border, is he?

Inevitability of young Scot asking pub landlady how she guessed.

Possibility of man wearing suede shoes and blazer joining conversation with claim that he himself is one-quarter Scottish on maternal grandparents' side, they having come from Perth.

Odds-on chance of eavesdropper to above exchanges asking should it be Scottish, Scotch or Scots, he can never remember which?

Likelihood of pub landlady saying whichever it is, there is some lovely scenery up there, contrary to the views of certain people who have never been further north than Watford and think it is all the Gorbals.

Prospect of saloon-bar raconteur now attaching himself to group and asking if young Scot has heard one, he can't do accent, about these two Jocks walking down Sauchiehall Street the noo, ye ken.

Absolute certainty of chap at end of bar, who has not hitherto spoken, prefacing rambling recollections of Aberdeen during war with elaborate request for permission to speak as mere Sassenach.

Likelihood of landlady saying that she has never been as far north as Aberdeen, but that she has been to Edinburgh, with its lovely castle and scones.

Possibility of man wearing suede shoes and blazer holding up empty glass to light as if examining it for fingerprints, and remarking that many myths attaching to Scottish, Scotch, or Scots, call them what you would, one about their alleged meanness has least foundation.

Inevitability of young Scot buying large round of drinks.

Tendency of group to expand to include small sozzled-looking individual in bowler hat, and fat port-and-lemon-drinking lady who enquires of young Scot what he has on under his kilt, even though he happens to be wearing designer jeans.

Absolute certainty of chaps, at end of bar recounting circumstantial anecdote about detachment of Argyll and Sutherland Highlanders dancing on tables at French bistro to celebrate end of war, when it was amply evident to delight of mademoiselles present that nothing was worn under kilt.

Probability of small sozzled-looking individual observing owlishly and repeating at intervals, that a man is a man for a'that.

Prospect of saloon bar raconteur enquiring if young Scot has any objection to Irish jokes, it being well known to all that Scots and Irish are quite close in many ways, well, let him put it this way, closer than what they are to English, only stop him if young Scot has heard it but there were these two Paddies who come up to London for day, begorrah.

Possibility of man wearing suede shoes and blazer asking young Scot if he could possibly cash small cheque to enable man wearing suede shoes and blazer to get round of drinks in, there being no one more contemptible to his mind than fellow who does not stand his corner.

Inevitability of young Scot asking man wearing suede shoes and blazer if he is quite sure twenty-five will be enough.

Likelihood of pub landlady, upon calling time, telling young Scot there will be a welcome for him in pub while ever and whenever he is in The Smoke, as she assures him London is known.

Probability of small sozzled-looking individual singing that there will be a welcome in the hillsides.

Odds-on chance of eavesdropper pointing out that above ditty is Welsh and singing, counterpoint, that he will tak high road while young Scot taks low road.

Possibility of man wearing suede shoes and blazer knowing small drinking club just round corner.

Inevitability of young Scot being among large swaying delegation heading for small drinking club.

Disposititon of fat port-and-lemon-drinking lady to hang on young Scot's arm, address him as her dear, and assure him that if he has not yet got fixed up with bed for night, he has only to say word, she really means it.

Inclination of small drinking club hostess to be exact replica of pub landlady who knows many Scots, all of them salt of earth.

Possibility of man wearing suede shoes and blazer murmuring to young Scot that if he may mark his card, it is cheaper to buy wine by bottle rather than individual glass.

Inevitabiity of young Scot purchasing magnum.

Prospect of saloon bar raconteur, protesting that he cannot have this, man of kilt drinking wine, he has never heard of such a thing, young Scot must have wee dram on him, no, he absolutely insists.

Inevitability of young Scot accepting wee dram as chaser.

Tendency of everyone thereafter, whether in group or not, to include wee dram for young Scot in rounds of drinks.

Inevitability of young Scot buying wee drams for everyone in club.

Likelihood of small drinking club hostess asking young Scot if he will accept glass of champagne with blonde lady in corner, as it is her birthday.

Inevitability of young Scot buying bottle of champagne and packet of Silk Cut for blonde lady.

Disposition of fat port-and-lemon-drinking lady to warn young Scot that he should not flash his money around as there are some funny people in club.

Absolute certainty of chap previously at end of pub bar, now at end of club bar, retailing long mugging experience.

Possibility of man wearing suede shoes and blazer suggesting incredibly complicated financial transaction whereby Scot tears up cheque he has been given, hands over further twenty-five pounds, and accepts post-dated cheque for fifty, signed J. Smith and made out to cash, which man wearing suede shoes and blazer forgot to pay into bank this morning.

Inevitability of young Scot discovering that he has lost sum of hundred and twenty pounds.

Probability of small sozzled-looking individual raising his glass to young Scot while intoning words easy come, easy go.

Inevitability of young Scot accusing small sozzled-looking individual, man wearing suede shoes and blazer, saloon bar raconteur, chap previously at end of pub bar, eavesdropper, fat port-and-lemon-drinking lady, blonde lady in corner, and small drinking club hostess of having conspired to steal his money.

Likelihood of small drinking club hostess telling man wearing suede shoes and blazer that she is very very sorry, but if his friend cannot behave himself she will have to ask him to leave.

Possibility of man wearing suede shoes and blazer denying that he is young Scot's keeper, and announcing that he himself has to see man about dog.

Inevitability of young Scot seizing man wearing suede shoes and blazer by collar with object of thrusting bottle down throat.

Inevitability of young Scot being ejected from small drinking club.

Tendency of surgical-spirit drinker staggering along Caledonian Road to be followed by young Scot addressing him as Jimmy.

Alias Smith and Jones

The tribe that makes up one per cent of the population of the English-speaking world is getting its own magazine . . . Just out is the first number of *Smith's Own Magazine*, published simultaneously in the US – at Fort Smith, Arizona – and Canada at Smithville, Ontario.

Daily Mirror

From: G. Lackey, Research and Development, Publications Division.
To: Sir Charles Pepperfield, Chairman and Managing Director.

Many thanks for the copy of *Smith's Own* which you picked up on your American travels, and for your memorandum requesting observations. Here, for what they are worth, are my comments:
1   I agree with you that this is an exciting new trend in publishing and that we ought to get in on the ground floor.
2   As you rightly suggest, the Jones market is the obvious one to aim at first. We have checked out your inspired 'guestimate' and confirm that there are indeed a great many people called Jones.
3   Your hunch that by the law of averages many of them must be loaded is one that I share wholeheartedly.
4   By pulling out all the stops we could launch this publication on the date you would prefer above all others, St David's Day. Although you say that the title *Jones's Weekly* is the first one you thought of and we could probably come up with something better, we all

think that *Jones's Weekly* is absolutely right and that we should settle for this on your masthead.

5   Printing half the magazine in Welsh is a bold and innovative idea which we will certainly be following up.

6   I have, at your request, tossed your suggestions for half a dozen articles at our editor, David Ap Jones for him to develop or reject as he chooses. He likes all of them very much. His particular favourite is 'Jones in History' but he also thinks that 'Jones In The Arts', 'Jones In Politics', 'Jones In Commerce' (good advertising tie-up here, as you shrewdly point out!), 'Jones In The Armed Forces' and 'Jones At The Old Bailey' are just as good, if not better.

7   In case you are wondering who David Ap Jones is, he is that very competent man called Arbuthnot who has changed his name by deed poll, while absolutely appreciating that his appointment did not hang on this move and that you were merely thinking aloud.

8   I like the slogan 'Keep Up With The Joneses' very much indeed, and we shall certainly use it in the launching campaign.

9   I also very much like the idea that the address of our subscriptions department should be a city with the name Jones in it, and you are absolutely spot on in your recollection that there is a place called Jonestown in Guyana. We go along one hundred per cent with this, our only reservation being that as Jonestown was recently the site of one of the biggest mass murders in modern history, it may not do for us what – say – Pleasantville does for the *Reader's Digest*. There is a Jonesville in one of the southern United States which may work for us two ways if we ever start a spin-off magazine for women called *Virginia*. Perhaps you could give us your valued judgement on this.

10   Turning now to the possibility of other titles, once *Jones's Weekly* has hit the bookstalls. I am in complete agreement with you that *Pepperfield's Magazine* seems the most logical development, and I do asssure

you that I say this only after heeding your wise counsel and putting the fact that your own name happens to be Pepperfield completely out of my mind. Although there are not so many potential readers called Pepperfield as there are Joneses, Browns or Robinsons, this can only be a plus, in that it puts us in the exclusive AB market, with all that this promises in prestige advertising.

11 I did not know that an artist called R. Pepperfield exhibited some water-colours of graves and tombstones at the Royal Academy in about 1893, but I will certainly chase this exciting find up. If you have any other ideas for illustrations or articles for *Pepperfield's Magazine*, they would be most welcome, and I am sure they would give our first issue a big boost.

12 May I ask the Circulation Manager to give your secretary a buzz when it is convenient? He has been unable to find any Pepperfields in the London telephone directory but believes that many of them, like yourself, may be ex-directory and that you may be able to give him some clue to their whereabouts. He is very thrilled at the prospect of getting his teeth into *Pepperfield's*.

13 I could not agree more that a glossy magazine called *Nigel* would have instant appeal to people of that name. I will certain sound out Mr Dempster. With your usual flair, you have hit on the perfect candidate for the editorial chair.

14 *Aubrey, Barbara, Clarence and Emma* will likewise make first-class additions to our stable of publications, and I am having dummies prepared at once. (Am I correct in thinking that you have children or grandchildren of these names? I hope we would not be accused of nepotism if we launched these titles with portraits of their real-life namesakes, and I am hoping to persuade someone of the calibre of Lord Snowdon, who I think would do us a first-class job. I have already taken the great liberty of sounding out this

little idea with your eldest son Mr Nigel Pepperfield, who as you know is to be editor-in-chief of this new series of titles, and he is very enthusiastic and has agreed to allow a full-length oil portrait of himself to be used as the first cover of Nigel, provided Mr Dempster – if we can get him – agrees.)

15 But as you stress with characteristic far-sighted-ness, it is in the field of surnames that the pickings will be richest. *Benson's Own*, *Hetherington's Fortnightly Review*, *Booth-Cottingley's Magazine*, *Pratt's News* and *Far-quar's Illustrated* are all tip-top ideas, and *McDougal's Weekly* should do especially well north of the border. You say these are 'merely' names you jotted down on your place-card at a dinner-party. All I can say, Sir, is that there is not a dud among them and that you have once again displayed your unerring instinct for pick-ing winners.

16 *Harper's*, however, has been done, as have *Dalton's Weekly*, *Lloyd's List* and *Annabel*. The fact that these are all highly successful publications shows that, as ever, our Chairman is on the ball.

17 The research assistant who told you that *Pearson's Weekly* had also been done was – if I may quote your own words – 'an incompetent nincompoop' and I apol-ogize for inflicting this ex-employee on you. If one wished to be pedantic, it could be argued that techni-cally there used to be a magazine called *Pearson's Weekly* which ran from 1890 to the 1940s, but it is now defunct. In any case, it was not aimed at readers called Pearson, so we have a clear field here.

18 I have followed up your invaluable suggestion that if we look up all the Pearsons in *Who's Who* and see what they list as their preoccupations and recrea-tions, we will have a module of the kind of reader we are aiming at. The editorial content of *Pearson's Weekly*, then should reflect an interest in mountaineering, foreign travel, all forms of sport, birdwatching, gar-dening, fishing (salmon and trout), music, and the

application of statistical method in problems of standardization and quality control. I think we are on to a winner here.

19 I will come right out and confess that I felt a moment of doubt at the Idea of *Lady Philippa Hedgeworth-Hawthorpe's Daily News*, as I know of only one Lady Philippa Hedgeworth Hawthorpe and that is your friend Lady Philippa Hedgeworth Hawthorpe. Then, of course, I realized that with your customary brilliance you had hit on the up-market publication to end all up-market publications. A quality newspaper with a circulation of one will be a feather in our cap indeed and we are taking your advice and finding out what it would cost to print it on vellum.

20 What can I say about X, the paper for people who don't want any publicity? Sheer genius, Sir! I will put it in hand at once.

I, Myself v My Father

Children in California may now take their parents to court in custody battles. 'Kids are soon going to be using lawyers to get *everything*,' warns one attorney.

News item

Before Lord Justice Bonniface, Mr Justice Trimmer and Mr Justice Dogood.

If a skateboard is left at the top of some stairs, and somebody's Father slip on the skateboard and twist his ankle, while vouchsafing (Jesus Christ) as well as (Aaaaaarrrggghhh!!!), he cannot stop a person's pocket money for 4 weeks just because, it was that person's Skateboard. This exclaimed by Lord Justice Bonniface in the appeal court, also Mr Justice Trimmer not to mention Mr Justice Dogood, they agreed with him.

Also, they gave me a toffee for telling the truth, and for not being frightened. I sat with them. They stated, (come up here little boy) and I did.

Their lordships dismissed an appeal by My Father against another Judge who say, that he has to give me my pocket money, and also that I can keep rabbits in my bedroom, also that it is Unnatural to expect Boys to be forever washing their Necks, also that not a shred of evidence to suggest that I touched his Whiskey. Also if he Hit me again, I have to tell my solicitor. This Judge gave me a humbug for being a Brave Boy and knowing what the Oath is. I sat with this judge as well, and he let me wear his wig.

LORD JUSTICE BONNIFACE say that he was not impressed by My Father's Demeanour in court. He go purple and start shouting, he ask if this British justice and also, that if it is, he will join the National Front or emigrate to Australia. I would like to go to Australia where there is much bush and koala bears are to be got. But, I would not go to Australia if they do not have Laws like ours for the reason that, My Father would get me. He would shoot poisoned Arrow at me whilst I was asleep, and, he would say it was the aboriginies.

Lord Justice Bonniface ejaculated that My Father's view that, (I need a good swift kick up the backside) was wholly irrelevant to the submissions by, the Appellant. The only question at issue was whether, the Judge had correctly interpreted the Law when that worthy awarded damages to I, myself. Lord Justice Bonniface retort that, the judge had based his decision on the precedent of (Appleyard *v* His Father). In the case just mentioned, it been a Roller-Skate on the Bedroom Lino instead of a Skateboard on the Landing, but, in Law, a Skateboard was the same as a Roller Skate, so when My Father skidded on it whilst uttering (Jesus Christ) as well as (Aaaaaarrrggghhh!!!) he should still have given me my pocket money. Coming to the end of his narrative, the Latter concluded, (Whilst Mr Appleyard appears to have suffered Multiple Contusions, the Appellant in this case can apparently walk quite well with the aid of a stick, when it suit his purpose to do so. Therefore the Appellant is dotty and also spotty.)

MR JUSTICE TRIMMER say he agree with the Latter. Mr Justice Trimmer maintained that he would Draw a Veil over My Father's behaviour in the witness Box. If the transcripts of his evidence were reliable, he Foam at the mouth when asked the reason why he thought that I, myself, gave his Whiskey to my Rabbits. This irrelevant as counsel should have known, therefore counsel silly and also pilly. Whatever the condition of the Rabbits on, the morning in question, it was not a Rabbit that My Father tripped over whilst explaining (Jesus Christ) as well as (Aaaaarrrggghhh!!!) but, it was a Skateboard. Therefore, the threat to confiscate my Rabbits was wholly unjustified, and a possible infringement of (The Discrimination Against Children Act 1977).

Warming to his tale, the Former continued that besides (Appleyard *v* His Father) the Judge could also have cited (Bullock *v* His Father, His Mother, His Grandmother and His Big Sister), where a Boy had been wrongfully locked in his bedroom just because, his Pet Vole had escaped. His Lordships say that, whilst my Father had not locked me in bedroom, also whilst Four Rabbits were not the same as a Pet Vole, also whilst the Pet Vole had merely run into the garden whereas, the Four Rabbits were Lurching around the Dining Room, My Father had expressly threatened violence, also he say (And another thing, those b*!%&y rabbits go back to b*!%&y pet-shop first thing tomorrow morning). Mr Justice Trimmer volunteered that, the papers should go to the director of

Public prosecutions, for the reason that, My Father had issued threats, this illegal under (Children's Equality Act 1977) I hope he get Seven Years Hard Labour. Mr Justice Trimmer also volunteer that, My Father's Belligerent Attitude when he wave his arms about and say that I, myself, should have been strangled at birth, did not do his case any good. Mr Justice Trimmer say it neither here nor there, but my Father should see a Doctor about his High Blood Pressure. I would be sorry if he die, but, if he in prison, they have prison Doctors. They could look after him and put him in a straitjacket when he go Purple.

The third denizen of the court, who had hitherto been strangely silent, then took up the story. He say that, he must reluctantly concur with his Brothers. He agreed that, the Appellant might be liable to Criminal Proceedings. He had been provoked beyond endurance, but, that no excuse in law, and, he was ill-advised to bring the case to appeal. The Appellant was therefore nutty and also putty.

Mr Justice Dogood add that the law was very clear on children's Rights. Parliament in its wisdom had laid it down that, children however precocious, they were equal under the law and it had provided them with the channels to prosecute their grievances. If My Father thought, that, the Law was Bad and also Mad, he should take matters up with his member of parliament, he should not chase I, myself, up and down the stairs with His Hairbrush. If he had not been chasing I, myself, he would not have slipped on the Skateboard whilst mouthing (Jesus Christ) as well as (Aaaaarrrggghhh!!!). That surely was the crux of the case, in so far as it concerned Whiskey, Rabbits, Skateboards and 4 weeks pocket money.

Mr Justice Dogood vouchsafe that, he would confine himself to the Neck-washing question. He had examined the Neck of I, myself, and he had little doubt, that one could grow Seed Potatoes in it. But, Boys since time Immemorial had had Tidemarks around their Necks and their Fathers might have Forcibly Scrubbed them, but, they did not threaten to Drown them. The court had heard the evidence of I, myself, that My Father had blustered (If he not got clean neck when I come home, I shall throw him in Reservoir), also he say to My Mother (Why you not lock him in coal-shed). Mr Justice Dogood vouchsafe that he not agree with Psychologist who stated (This could have Scarred I, myself, for Life), but, it is a clear breach of the peace. My Father therefore Guilty and also Wilty.

The Cratchit Factor

'Tiny' Tim was legless, to begin with. There is no doubt whatever about that. It was the fifth time in the space for half an hour that the Group Public Relations Adviser had lurched to his feet to propose a toast.

'God bleh, sev one,' slurred the popular 'Tiny', and slid under the top table.

Robert ('Bob') Cratchit, chairman and managing director, rose to reply.

'Viable product . . .' droned Cratchit. 'Cost-effective . . . marketing operation . . . retail outlets . . . growth rate potential . . . export thrust . . .'

The applause was thunderous.

What a sales conference it had been! What concepts, what projections, what plastic name-tags, what folders stuffed full of background briefing, what working breakfasts! What a sinking of double Scotches when the day's labours were over, what a sending to London for the prettiest secretaries to come down at once with this or that important file, what a tipping of Jenks (the Gatwick Coach-house International's amiable night-porter) to turn a blind eye! Such a-goings-on, such Rib Room dinings and Fisherman's Platter buffet luncheonings, such speechifying, such a-picking-up of Iberian air hostesses in Ye Post-horn Coffee Shoppe, had never taken place since the Cratchit Group had gone public.

Only Scrooge looked melancholy. Scrooge had been heard to say that the Psychology Seminar, wherein the reps had learned how to improve their sales by copying 'Tiny' Tim's limp, was humbug.

Alone among his colleagues, Scrooge did not sport a plastic name-tag. Oh no! Plastic name-tags were not for the likes of Scrooge! Scrooge had been born into this world without a label, was recognized on 'Change without a label, and would not suffer a label to adorn his person until that day came when a label was chiselled out for him in stone. Therefore few in the Cratchit Group knew exactly how Scrooge had been occupying himself ever since, following his nervous breakdown many years ago, he had turned up at his counting-house to find no counting-house there, and the warehouse turned into a wine-bar, and the firm of Scrooge and Marley taken over by his nephew.

There were those who said that Scrooge was retained as the office nark.

'Still having the bad dreams, Uncle?' asked Cratchit as he resumed his seat, signalling to the waiter to leave 'Tiny' Tim out of the next round of brandies.

'On and off, nephew,' responded Scrooge gloomily. 'The Ghost of Christmas Yet To Come still troubles me, especially after one of these office thrashes. It is a solemn Phantom, draped and hooded, that comes out of the mist towards –'

'Ever thought of having a check-up?' asked Cratchit hastily. 'There's a top-hat screening programme these days, you know – the full bit, Blood pressure, cardiograph, bronchoscope, liver tests, the lot. It's an in-house facility – why not use it?'

Scrooge was understood to remark that such arrangements were a waste of the company's money, and that he could not be doing with them and that they were humbug.

'The Ghost of Christmas Yet To Come was making an interesting performance projection analysis the other night,' Scrooge added. 'It was foreseeing the day when capital diverted to fringe benefits, added to your already soaring overheads plus your inability to claw back the cost of all these three-day promotional jags in four-star hotels, and bearing in mind the downward curve of profit-input, would – '

'Or,' interrupted Cratchit, 'there is always the Early Redundancy Plan. Nice golden handshake, index-linked pension, write off your company car – '

'While these rheumy old eyes can see,' said Scrooge firmly, pointing a quavering finger, 'I shall continue to serve the company in the capacity to which I am most – '

'I've been meaning to talk to you about that, Uncle,' said Cratchit. 'Change of policy. We don't mind anyone fiddling his swindle-sheet any more. In fact, with conventional incentives taxed out of existence, we encourage it. Top executives don't grow on trees, you know.'

'Nevertheless, nephew, I think you should be made aware to what extent your son "Tiny" Tim, is dipping into the petty cash float lately.'

'I told him to, you silly old muffin! Listen, he was offered £5,000 a year more by Dombey and Son (UK) Ltd. On his tax-band, that would have been £750 in his hot little hand. So instead of matching it, we gave him the key to the petty-cash box, and everyone's happy.'

'Belinda Cratchit, your daughter,' pursued Scrooge,

consulting a small black notebook, 'is having it off
rotten with the finance Director.'

'Keeps him happy. Dodson & Fogg, the investment
advisers, are after him for their Wall Street office.
Salary in dollars. I renegotiated his contract to include
an office penthouse, a Panther De Ville 4.2 convertible,
five weeks a year in Bermuda, and the use of Belinda.
He'll stay.'

'Master Peter Cratchit,' mouthed Scrooge, shielding
his face from the assembled merry makers with a
glossy brochure, 'has a black secretary.'

'Perk,' said Cratchit.

Scrooge, lips pursed in disapproval, put away his
notebook. 'I had a visit from old Marley the other
night,' he said. 'He wore the chains he had forged in
life, made link by link, and yard by – '

'You told me,' said Cratchit, snapping his fingers for
the bill.

'But did I tell you that he conducted me to a certain
counting house, where clerks were content to work
for wages their masters gave them, and where there
was no such thing as a company car, or a mortagage
assistance scheme, or a suit of clothes that technically
belonged to the firm but was rented to the employee
for a nominal sum; and where executives' wives were
not put on the pay-roll to provide a hidden salary
increase; and where credit cards were not strewn
about like confetti? Times,' said Scrooge, 'have
changed.'

'I'll drink to that,' said Cratchit, doing so.

At this point, there was a commotion, as a tall
young stranger in a soiled green coat that had
evidently once adorned a much shorter man, pushed
his way into the room, and he begged the company's
leave, and that they would excuse him for taking the
liberty, but he would insist upon having a word with
the chairman and managing director, and wouldn't
take no for an answer.

'Thousand pardons, sir,' commenced the stranger, approaching Cratchit. 'Forgive unwarrantable intrusion – realize am in completely wrong novel – but like your way of doing business, sir – temporarily disengaged – would be grateful for employment, very.'

Cratchit regarded the stranger coldly.

'Are there no Job Centres?' asked Cratchit.

'Plenty of Job Centres, sir – but—'

'And the unemployment benefits? Are they still in full vigour?'

'Believe so, sir.'

'Then sod off,' said Cratchit.

Meantime Scrooge was glumly examining the luncheon bill for £740 plus VAT and service charge, to which Cratchit had carelessly appended his signature.

'No good will come of this,' uttered Scrooge, to no-one in particular. 'The company is living beyond its means. Annual input twenty pounds, annual output nineteen pounds ninety-nine pee, result solvency. Annual input twenty pounds, annual output twenty pounds, one pee—'

Cratchit, having disposed of the stranger, turned to his sales director, David Copperfield.

'There's another one who doesn't know what bloody book he's living in,' he murmured. 'Now you're a bright spark, Dave: what do *you* think of the way I'm running this outfit?'

'It's a far, far better thing that you do, than you have ever done,' said the sales director.

Split Ends

Marriage breakdown is costing the State over £1,000 million a year, according to a report by the Society of Conservative Lawyers which urges the appointment of a Royal Commission into the problems of marriage and divorce.

Daily Telegraph

Minutes of Oral Evidence
Examination of Witnesses – 27th Day

8641 CHAIRMAN: Mrs Nirdwood, you are a housewife, are you not, and you place great store by the state of matrimony, believing as you do that two can live as cheaply as one and if I may quote from your admirably lucid written evidence, that love and marriage, they go together like a horse and carriage? MRS NIRDWOOD: DEFINITELY.

8642 LORD GOOSEBURY: You go on to say, Mrs Nirdwood, that one must remember this, a kiss is still a kiss, a sigh is still a sigh, and that the fundamental things apply as time goes by. It might perhaps benefit the inquiry if you would care to expand on that? MRS NIRDWOOD: It is our song. When Leonard and I were engaged, we used to go to the Lyceum ballroom of a Saturday. They played it all the time.

8643 PROFESSOR WAINSCOT: You are going back somewhat now, Mrs Nirdwood, if I may say so? – MRS NIRDWOOD: Oh, bless you, yes, more years than I care to remember. It has all changed now. It is all disco these days. Still, we are still together. That is the main thing.

8644 LADY VASE: What you are telling the Commission, Mrs Nirdwood, is that yours has been and indeed remains to this day, a very happy marriage? – MRS NIRDWOOD: Definitely.

8645 CHAIRMAN: It would assist us greatly, Mrs Nirdwood, if you could briefly itemize the ingredients of a happy marriage in your not inconsiderable experience? – MRS NIRDWOOD: Sharing. That and a sense of humour. You have to be able to laugh together, or you would go mad.

8646 SIR HENRY BLOTT: You are an exceedingly helpful witness, Mrs Nirdwood. Is there anything you would like to add to what you have told the Commis-sion? – MRS NIRDWOOD: Never sleep on a quarrel, and always cut your coat according to your cloth.

8647 LORD GOOSEBURY: Splendid, splendid! MRS NIRDWOOD: Thank you.

8648 LADY GOOSEBURY: So this is what you get up to when my back is turned, you filthy swine? CHAIRMAN: I think the Secretary ought perhaps to put it in the minutes here that Lady Goosebury has burst into the room at this point, that while it is always delightful to see Lady Goosebury she is not in fact either a member of this Royal Commission or one of our invited witnesses, and that she is brandishing what appears to be a rolling pin.

8649 MRS NIRDWOOD: You do not often see wooden ones in this day and age. It is all plastic. And the young wives you get these days, they cannot cook for toffee. That is why so many marriages are breaking down. The way to a man's heart is through his stomach. CHAIRMAN: Quite. If I may turn back to Lady Goosebury for a moment. I wonder if there is any comment she would like to put to the Commmission as to why she is interrupting these proceedings?

8650 LADY GOOSEBURY: He is having an affair

with that trollop. Go on, you beast, deny it if you can.
LORD GOOSEBURY: Ignore her, Mr Chairman. She has
been taking some pills for a nervous condition, and
these, combined probably with the sherry my wife
usually takes after breakfast, would, I think, account
for her present unfortunate behaviour.

8651 LADY GOOSEBURY: Yes, you sex-mad little
pervert, and tell the Commission *why* the woman who
married you when you had nothing and stood by you
all these years is taking pills for a nervous condition.
Go on, I dare you. LORD GOOSEBURY: Now stop it,
Helen. Pull yourself together.

8652 MRS NIRDWOOD: Excuse me, but am I needed
any more? Only I have promised to go up to Oxford
Street and get Leonard's mother a hot water bottle, as
hers has withered and we do not have a Boot's locally?
LADY GOOSEBURY: You slut, I wonder you can look
me in the face.

8653 PROFESSOR WAINSCOT: Does your mother-
in-law live with you at all, Mrs Nirdwood, and if so
would you regard that as a handicap or otherwise to a
successful marriage? MRS NIRDWOOD: She has lived
with us since her fall seven years ago. We get on very
well. I am very lucky in that respect. But then she is
not under my feet as she has her own granny flat.

8654 LADY GOOSEBERRY: Very convenient, the
brazen harlot. LORD GOOSEBURY: What do you mean
by that?

8655 LADY GOOSEBERRY: You know very well what
I mean. You have been going to that woman's house in
the afternoons and doing all the lewd things that you
used to do with me until I had a lock put on my
bedroom door. LORD GOOSEBURY: Don't be ridiculous.
You are mad.

8656 LADY GOOSEBURY: Then why does she write you letters about a kiss being a kiss, full of disgusting references to fundamental things? Go on, answer me that. LORD GOOSEBURY: You stupid, hysterical creature, that was Mrs Nirdwood's written evidence to the Commission. I brought it home to study.

8657 LADY GOOSEBURY: Brought it home to study, did you? The same way as you bring home all those perverted magazines, I suppose. Mr Chairman, he thinks I don't know where he hides them, but I do. And another thing, he dresses up in my clothes when I am out. LORD GOOSEBURY: She is deranged, Mr Chairman.

8658 SIR HENRY BLOTT: Arising out of this, perhaps I might ask Mrs Nirdwood if it is not too intrusive a question, whether she receives a dress allowance or whether she is expected to fend for herself out of her overall housekeeping allowance? LADY GOOSEBURY: Look at him sitting there as if butter wouldn't melt in his mouth. And all the time he is wearing one of our house-keeper's suspender belts. He took it from the clothes line.

8659 LORD GOOSEBURY: Helen, please. LADY GOOSEBURY, Oh it is Helen please, now, is it? It was not Helen please when you used to tie me to the wardrobe, was it? Drop your trousers, go on. If you are not wearing Mrs Robinson's suspender belt, drop your trousers, and prove it to the Commission.

8660 CHAIRMAN: Really, Lady Goosebury, we must get on now. LADY GOOSEBURY: I am sorry, I am making an exhibition of myself. I am so unhappy. I should have married you, Gerald.

8661 LORD GOOSEBURY: Gerald who? LADY VASE:

104

I believe that was a reference to our Chairman. Perhaps you would like to expand on that statement, Lady Goosebury? What exactly are you driving at when you say 'I should have married you, Gerald?'

8662 CHAIRMAN: She is insane – LORD GOOSEBERRY: You shut your mouth.

8663 MRS NIRDWOOD: *I* was engaged to a Gerald at one time, but he joined the Navy. Leonard and I laugh at it now! – PROFESSOR WAINSCOT: But you are not implying, Mrs Nirdwood, that you married Mr Nirdwood on the rebound, and even if you were, would you say that it is necessarily a bad start to a marriage?

8664 LORD GOOSEBURY: So it is Gerald, is it? I wasn't even aware that you even knew the Chairman of this Commission, apart from having met him occasionally at official cocktail parties. LADY GOOSEBURY: Official cocktail parties? Ha. You do not know the half of it.

8665 CHAIRMAN: I think this might be a suitable moment to adjourn for lunch? LADY VASE: Yes, I thought you'd say that. Have you been having an affair with this woman?

8666 LADY GOOSEBURY: What is it to you? Has he been stringing you along too? He is quite a success with the ladies, aren't you, Mr Chairman? LORD GOOSEBURY: I will throttle him.

8667 SIR HENRY BLOTT: Mrs Nirdwood, what importance do you put on fidelity in marriage? LORD GOOSEBURY: Take that, you philandering swine. And that, And that.

8668 CHAIRMAN: Ouch, Stop it. MRS NIRDWOOD: It

doesn't affect me one way or the other. I don't much go for the physical side personally, so long as I don't hear about it and he leaves me alone, I'm quite happy.

8669 CHAIRMAN: Thank you, Mrs Nirdwood, you have been most helpful. All right, Goosebury, you have asked for it. If the Secretary will be so kind as to hold my jacket . . .

Sinbad the Sailor

An historian who sailed the Atlantic in a leather boat to prove Irish monks could have done so 900 years before Columbus, said yesterday he was to make another voyage – in the wake of Sinbad . . .
    'He is undoubtedly the most famous sailor of all time, and I want to show that many of the stories about him could have been true,' said Mr Timothy Severin, who lives in Co. Cork.

Daily Telegraph

Day One

An uneventful start to my voyage, apart from a curious encounter at the quayside while we were taking on provisions. A strange middle-aged man, wearing a powdered wig, silk knee breeches and frogged livery, came up behind me as I stooped over a bag of oatmeal and tapped me lightly with his tipstaff. 'Whoops, did I catch you bending, ducky?' trilled this peculiar individual, rolling his eyes. He then confided that he was the personal servant of a gentleman who had sent him to enquire whether the Sinbad who was the subject of my voyage was by any happenchance that same cheeky monkey who had played the lead in the pantomine *Sinbad the Sailor* at the Grand Theatre, Cokeville, in 1953, only to abscond with the week's takings and a hamper of props, because if so the gentleman would like to sign on as the ship's cook under an assumed

106

name, with a view to confronting him on a dark stormy night.

I commanded the pouting poltroon to report to his master that the class of fiction into which I was preparing to sail was altogether superior to any that he might have been involved with in the touring theatres of the North of England, and that in any case, I had already engaged not only one but two ship's cooks, to wit that droll duo Buzby and Fuzby ('A Giggle A Minute').

Returning my attention to my vessel, I instructed the crew to man the bilge-pumps, whereupon my odd visitor once more struck me a mock blow with his wand, observed, 'Whoops, you filthy devil!' and minced off. Odd.

Wind: NE x E – Force 3. Lat: 48.32N. Long: 02.33W. 18m WSW of Needles. Drizzle.

Day Three

Everything shipshape. Sea calm. Handed the wheel over to my first mate so that I could inspect the mizzenmast. Thus unpreoccupied by routine, I noticed for the first time that the ship's cat is wearing fitted thigh-boots, which I am ready to swear was not the case when we set sail.

This was strange enough: yet when I asked the cat's custodian, the ship's carpenter, what it thought it was about, the affair became even stranger, for it was the animal itself which replied: 'Trying them out for thighs,' to which the carpenter, I know not why, added an expression new to me, 'Boom-boom!'

I at once asked this remarkable cat how it came to be able to speak passable English. The following exchange I record verbatim:

CAT: Because I'm wearing sea-boots.

MYSELF: Yes, I can see you're wearing sea-boots, you silly little feline, but how does wearing sea-boots miraculously turn you into a talking cat?

CAT: That's the wonder of wellies.
CARPENTER: Boom-boom.
This is going to be a rum voyage.
Wind: NW x W – Force 4. Lat: 49.56N. Long: 04.49W. 12m ESE of Lizard Point. Rain.

Day Six
On course and making good speed. Repaired tear in mainsail. After an outbreak of pilfering, found forty Arabians stowing away in jars. Locked them in hold.
Wind: SE – Force 4. Lat: 50.28N. Long: 12.32W. 72m WSW of Fastnet. Hail.

Day Nine
Was obliged to remind that priceless pair Buzby and Fuzby ('A Giggle A Minute') that I am the captain and that they take their orders from me. Matters came to a head when, after my lunch failed to materialize, I asked the crazy couple why I had not been served.

It was Buzby (the thin one) who riposted: 'Served? What do you think we are, guv, flipping tennis players?' To this Fuzby (the fat one) added irreverently, 'They also serve who only stand and wait,' at which Buzby retorted – and I made a careful note of his insolent words – 'And we're not flipping waiters, neither, so I'm not standing for that.'

Reminding him that we were on the high seas, where there is such an offence as mutiny, I asked the titterful twosome in no uncertain manner what the devil they were doing out of uniform and why they were wearing green baize aprons. The insubordinate statements appended were made in front of a witness, the ship's carpenter:
BUZBY: Why are we wearing green baize aprons? Why are we wearing green baize aprons? My my, you are green! We're wearing green baize aprons, you higneramus, because we are the broker's men.
MYSELF: You're the broker's men?

BUZBY: We're the brokers' men!
FUZBY: And we've come to tell you you're broke!
CARPENTER: Boom-boom.

For all that this was an open display of defiance, it
would have been foolhardy of me to have tried to have
Buzby and Fuzby ('A Giggle A Minute') clapped in
irons, for with such weak material they must have
been confident that they had the support of the ship's
chorus, as the crew now prefers to call itself. Accordingly, since they still refused to serve lunch, I sent
them about their business and opened a tin of
sardines.
*Wind: SE – Force 4. Lat: 45.24N. Long: 21.07W. 65m WSW
of Baron Hardup's Castle. Light applause.*

Day Ten
Continued on course with excellent sail. Night sky
clear. I think I am going mad.

To quote to this log but one example: at six bells
today the ship's cat , which as well as wearing boots
had now taken to carrying all its possessions tied in a
spotted handkerchief on the end of a stick, appeared
for its morning herring accompanied by a young
person, dressed as a boy from the waist up but
wearing fishnet tights, who as they entered the cabin
was slapping his/her thighs and exclaiming jauntily,
'But can't you hear the bells, you silly puss; unless we
turn back now we'll miss the bus!' I was so taken aback
that I mentioned to the two broker's men – ably played
by Buzby and Fuzby ('A Giggle A Minute') – who now
occupy my cabin, that I must be going out of my mind.
Immediately, a fruity, bassoprofundo voice responded,
'Oh, no you're not!' Unaccustomed as I am to being
contradicted, I averred, 'Oh, yes I am!' whereupon the
unseen interloper came back with, 'Oh, no you're not,
is he, children?' from I know not where there was a
resounding chorus of 'No!' Followed by loud cheers,
followed by the fruity voice complaining, 'Ooh, me

stays! Ooh, me unmentionables! Ooh, I feel all of a doodah!' and so on. At my sharp enquiry of 'Who was that? Who are you?' the unseen voices yelled, 'Behind you!' and through the porthole strugged a stowaway dressed as a washerwoman. She gave her name as a Mrs Twankey and her status as that of widow. I had her put in the hold with the forty Arabians.

Wind: NW – Force 3. Lat: 46.35N. Long: 22.36W. 18m ESE of the Enchanted Forest. Laughter.

Twelfth Incredible Day

Two more stowaways – mere babes, found by the ship's carpenter among some wood. Despite their youth, I had to make an example of them, since there is no more room for further walk-on parts in the hold, so I gave them the option of walking the plank or climbing the beanstalk. They chose the latter course. As I said to the first mate:

I think that we should have no fears,

We've seen the last of *those* poor dears!

Heh heh heh, if I may permit myself the expression. That tiresome piece of administration completed, I went and tried on the new red uniform which the purser kindly obtained for me, having been granted three wishes by a genie he encountered in the lamp-locker. The horns need stiffening, and the tail will have to be taken up, otherwise it is a perfect fit.

Wind: NW – Force Fe Fi Fum. Lat: 48.06N. Long: 24.32 W. 22m WSW of Intermission. Reprise.

Third Record-breaking Week

(Voyage Must End Sat)

Sea choppy. The first mate, who has now revealed himself to be a prince in disguise, has asked permission to hold a glass slipper contest in the mess. I see no harm in that: if I have kept my charts correctly, we should shortly be in sight of the Finale, and can afford a little relaxation. I decided that a ship's concert would be in order. Accordingly, all the boys and girls on the starboard side, led by Buzby and Fuzby ('A Giggle A Minute') were asked to sing 'The Hills Are Alive With The Sound of Music', while all the boys and girls on the port side, led by two ugly sisters who apparently wandered on board mistaking us for a cruise to Majorca, sang, 'I've Got a Luverly Bunch Of Coconuts'. Small prizes of sweets were thrown to the side singing loudest.

Meanwhile, the ship's carpenter had constructed a huge staircase which lights up, and we all walked down it, in reverse order of seniority. As I escorted Widow Twankey and the ship's cat down the glittering stairs, what should appear in the sky but a great auk, suspended from a rope, with no less a personage than Sinbad the Sailor himself on board, waving furiously. As they continued to circle our vessel, a great curtain of fog descended; it rose again and we all bowed; it descended and rose again several times; the applause was deafening. We were all delighted by the success of our voyage and are already talking about touring Australia with it.

Wind: SW – Gales of laughter. Lat: 49.23N. Long: 35.27WE. 1m ESE of Transformation Scene. Standing ovation.

The Fix

or: Report of the Commission on the Environmental and Economic Effects of an International Airport at Doncaster.

Lord Porchester says he tried to make his official report on Exmoor read like a thriller by Dick Francis. 'I tried to leave an unanswered question at the end of each chapter so that people would be forced to read on.'

Sunday Telegraph

Introduction

1   The Government's intention to appoint a Commission to inquire into the problems of a new international airport on the site of Doncaster racecourse was announced by the then President of the Board of Trade on 23rd February 1978.

2   No sooner had the President of the Board of Trade made his announcement than there was a whistling sound followed by a sharp crack. The consensus view of Hon Members was that it was Concorde flying overhead, but the Commission, sitting in the Strangers' Gallery, had a different theory.

3   Someone, the Commission did not know who, was trying to nobble the President of the Board of Trade.

Chap 1   The Problem

4   Our task, as we saw it, was threefold. It was to suggest answers to the following questions:

(a)   Could the stimulus to tourism, trade and employment engendered by a new airport be expected to outweigh the economic shortfall caused by the closure of the racecourse?

(b)   What would be the environmental effects upon the area not only of the proposed airport, but the concomitant feeder road and service areas?

(c)   Who was the man with the livid scar on his left cheek who entered the dining-car at Watford and followed the Commission to Yorkshire?

Chap 2   Method of Approach

5   From the outset, the Commission was conscious of the need to establish public confidence that its work would be impartial.

6   It was decided therefore to institute a series of public hearings in a hall conveniently near Doncaster racecourse, where a member of the Commission could conceal himself in the loft and take secret photographs of all who gave evidence.

7   You never knew who might turn up at these public hearings!

Chap 3   Written Evidence

8   The Commission also considered a wealth of written evidence including memoranda from the Churches Committee on Gambling, the British Airports Authority, A Friend, and the Meteorological Office. The memoranda ranged from 185 pages of closely-typed foolscap to a portion of sugar bag on which capital letters cut out from newspapers and magazines had been pasted.

9   The bulk of the written evidence is summarized in Appendix I. The remainder has been sent to the police.

10   The Commission was impressed by the argument

advanced from several quarters that the environmental loss caused by the closure of the racecourse would be offset by the enhanced status of Doncaster as an important convention centre arising from its accessibility as an international air terminus.

11   The Commission was not impressed by the argument that it should get out of town and stay out of town if it knew what was good for it.

Chap 4   Oral Evidence

12   The Commission heard oral evidence from 135 individuals and representatives of organizations.

13   Mr G. Forsyth, for the Friends of the Earth, produced noise contour maps to support the view that the Doncaster flight paths would increase noise levels by some 4PNdB.

14   The Rural Dean of Bruddersford, in his capacity as President of the Privet League, produced statistics to prove that gambling was a social evil. The Rural Dean's case was that the closure of the racecourse itself would be desirable, irrespective of any proposals to provide honest employment by developing an international airport.

15   The Chief Constable of Yorkshire expressed fears that a new airport would attract touts, gypsies and pickpockets. The Chief Constable stated that the Doncaster Police force was already seriously undermanned and that he could not guarantee law and order in the various departure lounges, duty-free shops and the remainder which would become the haunt of airport gangs.

16   Although the fact was not germane to our enquiry, the Commission could not help noticing that the Chief Constable of Yorkshire did not pronounce any of his aitches, and that he had a livid scar running down his left cheek.

17   The Commission had seen this gentleman before!

18   Mr L. T. Ramsbottom, for Doncaster District

Council, confirmed that land adjacent to the race-course, required for Runway Three, could be adequately drained.

Chap 5   Enter Mister Big

19   The decisive question of adequate drainage provision for Runway Three was re-examined on the final day of the Inquiry, when Mr Honest Jack Tomlinson, a turf commission agent, gave evidence.

20   Speaking in a personal capacity, Mr Tomlinson said that he could make it worth the Commission's while to give the thumbs down to the airport proposals. All the Commission would have to say was that the land could not be properly drained and Bob would be the Commission's uncle.

21   In consideration of the Commission reporting negatively on the desirability of the international airport on the site of Doncaster racecourse, Mr Tomlinson was prepared to pay the sum of £1000 (one thousand pounds) to each member of the Commission.

22   The witness was informed that accepting bribes was outside the Commission's brief.

23   While this point was being explained by the Chairman of the Commission, a knife whistled through the air and embedded itself in the oak panelling behind the Chairman's ear. At the same time, a gypsy was seen leaving the public gallery.

24   It was a superb make-up job. Someone had really worked on that gypsy disguise. But he had forgotten one thing.

25   Under the walnut staining on his left cheek ran a livid scar.

Chap 6   Conclusions

26   After considering all the evidence available, we were drawn inevitably to the following conclusions:

   (a)   Given that the projection of air traffic provided in the research paper (see Appendix II: Forecasts of

Air Traffic Demand at Heathrow, Gatwick and Manchester) is accurate, a new international airport will have become a necessity by 1981.

(b)   The unknown assailant who shot at the President of the Board of Trade, the man with the livid scar who followed the Commission to Doncaster, the anonymous letter-writer, the so-called Chief Constable of Yorkshire, and the 'gypsy' who threw a knife at the Chairman of the Commission are one and the same (see Appendix III: The Man With A Thousand Faces).

(c)   Despite the loss of an important recreational amenity that would of necessity be entailed, Doncaster is the best available site for a future airport.

(d)   Contrary to the impression that may have been given in the sub-heading 'Enter Mister Big', Mr Honest Jack Tomlinson was only a pawn in the game. He is a side-kick of the man with the livid scar, who is a Mr Mad Jack Harris.

(e)   Mr Mad Jack Harris controls a racecourse gang which derives a considerable portion of its income from equestrian events. Hence his desire to scotch this Inquiry.

(f)   The migratory Pontefract Goose nests near the projected Runway Two and the threat to bird-life in the area must be considered. This was, however, outside the scope of the Inquiry.

(g)   Mr G. Forsyth, who purported to give evidence on behalf of the Friends of the Earth, and the gentleman who presented himself as the Rural Dean of Bruddersford, are imposters. They are in reality the notorious leaders of a rival racecourse gang to the one controlled by Mr Mad Jack Harris. Their purpose in attending the Inquiry was to precipitate the closure of Doncaster racecourse with the object of forcing Mr Harris to do battle with them for the control of Newmarket and Plumpton.

Chap 7 Minority Report

27 A minority report, dissenting from the Commission's main conclusions, is published separately. The following are its salient points:

(a) The suggestion that a shot was fired at the President of the Board of Trade emanates from the Chairman of his Commission and the Chairman of this Commission only.

(b) The man with the livid scar and 'Mr Honest Jack Tomlinson' are professional actors. They were seen dining with the Chairman of the Commission at the latter's club shortly before the Inquiry began to accept evidence.

(c) It is well known that the Chairman of this Commission has been canvassing advice on how to get a bit of pep into his Report.

(d) It is a monstrous libel to suggest that Mr Forsyth of the Friends of the Earth and the Rural Dean of Bruddersford are imposters. In the view of this Minority Report the allegation was made by the Chairman of the Commission solely in order to lend colour to a chapter of Conclusions that was flagging badly after his invented revelations about the man with the livid scar.

(e) The Commission's pretended concern for the Pontefract Goose is a smoke-screen intended to draw attention away from the fact that an airport at Doncaster would have serious consequences for the sport of pigeon-racing. The Commission should take note that the Pigeon Fancy has powerful friends. The Commission has been warned.

Killing Time

Time just flew after a 34-year-old woman with influenza was told by her doctor, 'Stay in bed until I call round again.' For the Doctor forgot to come back . . . and the invalid stayed put for another FORTY YEARS.

News item

Dr Snodworth, you have been called before the Medical Disciplinary Council to answer a charge of negligent conduct in a professional respect. Do you have anyone to represent you?

I will defend myself, thank you.

Very well. Doctor, did you before you commenced general practice swear a certain oath by Apollo the physician, by Aesculapius, by Hygeia, Panacea and all the gods and goddesses?

I did.

Would you say that your professional conduct in respect of Mrs Louisa Edith Bellows, of Fern View, Parsonage Lane, London SW23PV 6YQ was compatible with that oath?

I would.

Would you tell the committee when you last made a house call upon Mrs Bellows?

Certainly, if I may consult my diary. It was on 11 April 1908. She had sent me a telegram complaining of stomach cramps.

You examined the patient and reached a diagnosis, did you?

I formed an opinion, yes. She had abdominal spasms with inflammation of the peritoneal lining consistent with her husband having put rat-poison in her cocoa.

What did you prescribe Dr Snodworth?

An emetic of grns 20 sulphate of zinc, followed by a course of perchloride of iron with solution of ammonia in equal parts, at the same time washing out the stomach and calling the police. I also advised Mrs Bellows to remain in bed and drink no more cocoa until she heard from me again.

I do not want to lead you, doctor, but the next time you saw Mrs Bellows was on 17 October this year, was it not?

That is correct. She hobbled unannounced into my surgery waving her stick and stating that if this was the bloody National Health Service, I could put it where the monkey put its nuts.

Did you examine her?

Yes.

What did you find?

Bed-sores.

Would you care to tell the committee, doctor, why you allowed a period of seventy years and six months to elapse between examinations?

By all means. When I left Mrs Bellows on 11 April 1908, I took with me a sample of cocoa dregs, meaning to post it at once to Mr Alphonsus Tooth.

Who is Mr Alphonus Tooth?

He is, or was, an analytical chemist. These days he is perhaps better known as the founder of Tooth's Bargain Basket Supermarkets. For the moment, suffice it to say that 11 April 1908 fell on a Sunday.

What is the significance of that, Dr Snodworth?

You are asking me to account for the delay between my house-call on Mrs Bellows and the subsequent re-examination. I had no stamps, and the post offices were closed. I was not able to despatch the sample of cocoa dregs to Mr Tooth until the following day, the 12th.

That accounts for twenty-four hours, doctor. What about the remaining seventy years, five months, and twenty-nine days?

I am coming to that sir. On 11 May, in response to a postcard reminding him that the results of his analysis were required urgently, as a patient's life might be at stake, Mr Tooth wrote me that the sample of cocoa-dregs had never arrived. I questioned my housemaid, who swore she had posted the package as instructed, but in a pillar-box notorious in the district for His Majesty's mails being regularly eaten by snails. I went at once to the pillar box, where sure enough I found a dead snail. I examined it, and its eyeballs were distended, consistent with the luckless mollusc having ingested a large quantity of poisoned cocoa.

At the risk of cutting your narrative short, Dr Snodworth, the committee has an affidavit from Miss Elizabeth Benedict, sometime sub-postmistress in the Lewisham area, to the effect that you tried to send a dead snail to an address in West London by registered post, and that she had to remind you of the Post Office regulations applying to obnoxious materials.

That is correct. There was quite a scene.

Never mind the scene, doctor. What did you do with the dead snail?

I gave a cabman, one Hodgson, a shilling to take it directly to Mr Tooth's laboratory.

What happened next, Dr Snodworth?

Two days later, on 13 May – I hope the committee will note how time was slipping by through no fault of my own – an angry Hodgson barged into my surgery demanding "ere, guv, what abaht my 'orse?"

It seems that people make a habit of walking into your surgery unannounced, doctor. What was the nature of the cabman's complaint?

I did not examine him, but he had a flushed countenance and a swaying gait consistent with being blind raving drunk.

I meant his complaint as regards the horse, Dr Snodworth.

Oh, I see. It appears that the dead snail had somehow fallen out of the cabman's waistcoat pocket into the horse's nosebag. Instead of obeying my instructions to go at once to Mr Tooth's, Hodgson had repaired to the Goat and Compasses public house for refreshment. He remained there until informed by a chimney-sweep that his horse had fallen on its side and was panting.

Did you examine the horse?

Sir, I am a registered medical practitioner with degrees from London and Edinburgh, and the author of a paper, 'Enlargement of the Sterno-mastoid Muscle In A Patient Who Reported A Nose-bleed In 1903 And Was Told To Sit With His Head Well Back Until The Doctor Could Find Time To Come Round And

Put A Key Down His Neck'. I am not a vet.

I beg your pardon, doctor. I will rephrase the question. Having learned that the horse was ill, probably as a result of having ingested the snail, what did you then do?

I joined the navy.

Any particular reason, Dr Snodworth?

To see the world. Also, because things were getting on top of me: My fiancée, a Miss Davenport, had recently broken off our engagement, my practice was suffering because of my deep personal unhappiness, I was very worried about Mrs Bellows and I felt in need of a complete change. I scribbled a note to Mr Tooth asking him to analyse the contents of the cabman's horse's stomach, then signed on as a surgeon-lieutenant on the cruiser Hermaphrodite.

You made it quite plain to Mr Tooth that as soon as you had a yea or nay from him on whether the horse was suffering from the effects of poisoned cocoa, you would obtain shore leave and pay another visit to Mrs Bellows?

Yes, I did. Unfortunately, we sailed for Madagascar on the high tide.

What did you do then, doctor?

I had many adventures. I fought in the Dardanelles campaign, acquired a Turkish mistress and met Lawrence of Arabia. I got drunk one night in Port Said and woke up in 'Frisco. I panned for gold, struck oil instead and lost all I possessed on the turn of a card. I was cowboy, prizefighter, speakeasy bar-keep and Skid Row bum. In 1927, chancing to meet a man by the name of Al Jolson, who had just made a film called The Jazz Singer, *I decided to try my luck at—*

When did you return to these shores?

In 1968, when I at once despatched another postcard to Mr Tooth asking if he had yet reached a conclusion about the contents of the horse's stomach. I found an England transformed, gentlemen. It was an era of motorways, Carnaby Street, boutiques and doubles bars. Gone were the slums. Tower blocks, like pointing fingers—

In short, doctor, you found that Mr Tooth had

expanded his small chemist's shop into a chain of supermarkets, and had retired to Guernsey. Did you, after establishing this to your own satisfaction, write to the company's Director of Public Relations?

Yes, asking if the former chairman had said anything about a dead or seriously-ill cab-horse. I received a printed acknowledgement.

And you have heard nothing since?

No sir. I decided to wait a little while longer and then advise Mrs Bellows that it was probably all right for her to get up provided she took it easy for the first few days. Then on 17 October, of this year, just as I was packing my stethoscope to pay her a visit, she arrived at my surgery.

Thank you, Dr Snodworth. I cannnot anticipate the committee's findings, but I am sure that having given us this lucid account, you should have no further cause for anxiety.

Curious Yellow

Romance is too much a preoccupation of Chinese literature, theatre and cinema today and it is sick, the Communist Party newspaper *People's Daily* declared in a commentary on the current artistic scene.

While love has its place in literature as well as life, it should always be kept 'under control' and in 'a proper ideological context' the paper said, continuing the party's campaign against bourgeois liberalism.

Guardian

A worker in the dairy collective, one Wu-Tzu-nung, went to the house of Fan Hsi-ying to deliver milk and strawberry-flavoured curds. But Fan Hsi-Ying was toiling in the fields, and so it was his wife who received Wu-Tzu-nung. She wore only a silk robe and stockings of fish-net.

Wu gave her the milk and curds. 'I have other things

122

on my cart, Mrs Hsi-ying,' said he. 'Perhaps you would like a carton of Blossom Of The New Dawn orange juice for your sons?'

Mrs Hsi-ying replied: 'I have no sons, but I would not mind some of the other.'

Presently Fan Hsi-ying returned from the fields. He was angry to find his house filled with dairy produce.

'Wife,' scolded Fan Hsi-ying. 'Where is the point of stocking up on Victory Of The Peasant Movement Over Ignorance blackcurrant essence and brick upon brick of Comrade Softee ice-cream when we have no sons to consume such scarce resources?'

'How do you expect me to bear you sons when you come home so tired from the fields each night that you wish only to sleep?' raged Mrs Hsi-ying.

Fan Hsi-ying continued to tirade against his wife. 'And another thing. What is that dairy collective worker's blue striped apron and pictograph-front underpants doing under our bed-roll?'

So the quarrel went on. Fan Hsi-ying was late back to the fields from his dinner break and that day did not complete his hoeing norm.

The conflict could have been avoided and productivity kept at the required level had Mrs Hsi-ying worked alongside her husband in the fields. A wife who has no sons should not spend her days in idleness, nor put on stockings of fish-net, which are symbolic of the feudal-patriarchal ideology all women must struggle to overthrow.

Petal Tien-chi and Brian Pao-chen lived in adjoining houses and belonged to the same youth cadre. It was always understood that when Brian had completed his studies at medical school and become a neurologist and part-time road-mender, he would take Petal to be his wife. In the meantime, she was content by day to work at the Prosperity Through Better Understanding Of The Need For Overall Planning pick 'n' match trousers of denim boutique, and in the evenings to read her magazine serial, 'On The Correct Handling Of Contradictions In Knitting Patterns.'

One morning, a handsome stranger, a salesman of etymological lexicons from a neighbouring province, came into the boutique to buy trousers of denim. His name was Chen-Hsu-lin. He flirted with Petal, asking if there were any more at home like her. At first Petal did not understand. She replied solemnly that she had three brothers. But soon the yen dropped, and she began laughing and joking with Chen Hsu-lin. Her life had been boring with Brian Pao-chen away at medical school and she was glad to have found a new friend. They arranged to see a film, *The Confessions Of A Polisher Of Windows.*

The time came for Chen Hsu-lin to pack up his etymological samples and move on. Petal was philosophical. 'It has been fun while it lasted,' she observed. Besides, there might be other handsome strangers coming into the trousers of denim boutique . . .

With the full moon, however, Petal became agitated. She grew tearful and morose, and was discovered by her mother sitting in a hot bath drinking rice wine. Brian was sent for. Petal flung herself into his arms. 'Oh Brian,' sobbed Petal. 'As a medical student, you must help me, or I shall have a baby.'

'Surely the reverse would be the case,' argued Brian. 'But as we are not yet married, you are merely stating a hypothesis.'

They discussed the matter far into the night, but Brian could not understand what his fiancée was talking about. The next day he returned to medical school and Petal drowned herself.

Ignorance is the rabid dog at the gate of progress. But while it is essential to educate the masses so as to serve the particular needs of the people as laid down by the Central Committee, there is over-specialization at the medical schools. Brian Pao-chen's extensive studies of the nervous system had left him unequipped to advise his fiancée. For her part, Petal Tien-chi was also the victim of ignorance. Young persons in the cities must be taught the merits of a negativist approach to handsome strangers selling etymological lexicons.

Three couples, the Chings, the Chungs and the Changs, went to the house of the Chengs where they drank wine.

By and by Mr Cheng, who had recently been allowed to travel to Hong Kong to visit a sick relative, said: 'I have learned a Western game. To begin with, we all throw our car keys into a chalked ring.'

He explained the rules of the game and the others grew excited. Then Mrs Ching grew sad.

'We none of us own cars,' she pointed out. The observation was incontrovertible and shortly afterwards the party broke up.

There is no place in the socialist system for material advance where this does not go hand in hand with the ideological advance of the people.

Wang Chi-weng, the manager of a rice-growing co-operative, was accustomed when he had closed his ledgers for the day to visit a wine-house. There he would meet Fifi La-tsung, a friend. Often, after they had drunk a bottle of Celebration Of The Shifting Of The Power Base From The Middle To The Poor Classes champagne, Want Chi-weng would complain to Fifi La-tsung: 'My wife, Madge Chi-weng gets these blinding headaches, and does not understand me. I cannot rectify the position by asking for a divorce, since she would take the mistaken step of killing herself. Yet there are those who would criticize me for taking solace in the wine-house.'

Fifi La-tsung would beg Wang not to reproach herself, counselling him: 'While it is contradictory to the broad principles of our democratic revolution to find expression in pleasure seeking, there is nothing wrong in having a good time provided this is practised with prudence as well as diligence, dearie.'

Wang Chi-weng spent many happy hours with Fifi La-tsung and bought her a coat of fur and other gifts.

But one night when he returned to his house after a supper with Fifi at the Just Good Friends People's Restaurant, Wang found his wife waiting up for him.

Madge Chi-weng chided her husband thus: 'Pay attention! You think I do not know of the situation that has arisen behind my back. This is a fundamental error. I know all about you and your fancy woman and her coat of fur.' With this Mrs Chi-weng brandished a revolver.

Her husband advised her urgently that she would solve nothing by shooting herself and that she should study the problem of their marriage afresh. But Mrs Chi-weng only laughed and said: 'I am not going to shoot myself, husband, I am going to shoot you,' and at once did so.

This was incorrect and cost the rice-growing co-operative a good worker. Instead of killing her husband Mrs Chi-weng should have gone to the rice-growers' committtee and explained the situation. The committee would then have examined Wang Chi-weng's ledgers to discover where he got the money to buy coats of fur.

Two reporters from the *The News of the Masses* visited a certain house where certain women were entertaining certain officials in a certain way. Having seen certain things, they made an excuse and left.

Metaphor, analogy and allegory are all useful tools of the Communist working in the mass movements, but it is counter-productive to be over-literal in the application of propaganda. The people's struggle does not mean being tied to a bed-post.

The Rough, the Green and the Ugly

A shower of five-pound notes, in all essentials not unlike senior snowflakes, fluttered through the clubhouse window on a light breeze and woke the Oldest Member from the doze into which he had fallen.

'I perceive,' observed a Scotch-and-soda who had strolled in from one of the Mulliner stories, 'that it is raining fivers.'

The Sage motioned him to a chair.

'If I have warned Angus McAngus to zip up the ball compartment of his golf bag once, I have warned him a hundred times. Yet he continues to scatter five-pound notes as if they were rose-petals strewn in the path of Min, the fertility god.'

The Scotch-and-soda looked baffled.

'The connection eludes me. Am I to understand that Angus McAngus carries five-pound notes in the ball compartment of his golf bag?'

'Not invariably,' concluded the Oldest Member. 'On some occasions he may add the spice of variety to the procedure by carrying tenners. On others, notes of an even larger denomination. It depends whom he wishes to bribe.'

'Bribe? Did you say bribe?'

The Oldest Member, retrieving a neglected five-pound note from the waste paper basket with the sharp-sightedness of a well-trained pig which has detected a truffle in the undergrowth, agreed that he had said bribe.

'I need not add that Angus McAngus has become a hissing and a byword wherever property speculators with a handicap of less than four assemble. Our members frown on sordid cash transactions. They prefer to grease the palms of the planning committee either with post-dated cheques or with the offer of an

127

asssisted passage to the Bahamas. This is, after all is said and done, a club for gentlemen.'

'Planning committee? Is that the same as the Cups, Trophies and Tournaments committee?'

'It is not, but it may well be,' replied the Sage, shaking his head gravely. 'Most of our little tournaments nowadays are played between council planning officials and property dealers or owners of large tracts of land. It has even been mooted that Rule 7(b) should be altered so that the President's Cup shall in future be awarded to the first member to land a building contract under par.'

The Scotch-and-soda clicked his tongue in fair imitation of a hen reproving her chicks for not eating up their chopped worm.

'I remember this club,' he said, 'when the only hint of what might be termed hanky-panky was when Alexander Pervington, in order to win the hand of Evangeline Ffitch-Mortimer by causing her rival Gwendoline Prendergast to lose the Ladies' Spring Medal competition and thus seek solace in the arms of Wilbur Foskitt to whom Evangeline had become engaged in admiration of his brassie shots, was suspected of switching divots on the sixteenth and seventeenth holes. Are you telling me that times have changed?'

The Oldest Member pointed a quavering finger to the far horizon.

'Do you see the block of offices yonder?'

'If you mean the excrescence that dominates the fairway like an enlarged carton of breakfast cereal,' said the Scotch-and-soda with a shudder, 'you may depend upon it that it has not escaped my notice.'

'That edifice,' continued the Oldest Member, 'owes its existence to a foursome consisting of Rollo Pendlebury, the chairman of the district council in our little backwater here; our popular planning officer Lancelot (Tubby) Catherspoon; one Septimus Purvis, of Purvis,

Purvis, Purvis and Purvis, the Mayfair development consortium; and a certain Jasper Potts, who is by way of being a building contractor.

'Pendlebury had been practising his back-swing and confidence gleamed from his spectacles as he strode, in much the same manner as Tennyson's hard heir strode about the lands and would not yield them for a day, to the first tee. His opening drive—'

'Excuse me,' interjected the Scotch-and-soda in some agitation. 'This isn't a short story by any chance, is it?'

The Sage regarded his listener with the narrow eye of a life president of the Worshipful Company of Plumbers who, upon encountering a youthful slug in the U-bend of a kitchen drain, suspects it of gate-crashing.

'I was merely about to give you a short resumé of the match,' he said coldly. 'If you do not wish for details, suffice it to say that Pendlebury and Cather-spoon took the first, third, fourth, fifth, seventh, ninth, twelfth and thirteenth holes, while Purvis and Potts accounted for the second, the sixth, the eighth, the tricky tenth water-hole, the eleventh and the fourteenth, where they conceded the game.'

'I don't see what this has to do with blocks of flats,' said the Scotch-and-soda sulkily.

'I was coming to that. A cheque for twenty thousand pounds exchanged hands in the clubhouse. I will give you another example,' added the Oldest Member hurriedly as his visitor rose to leave. 'I believe you have just come from the Angler's Rest?'

'Yes, I was driven out by Mulliner, who was about to embark on an interminable yarn about his nephew, Brandreth.'

'Then,' continued the Oldest Member, unperturbed, 'you cannot have failed to notice the £15,000,000 Leisure Complex directly across the road from the Angler's Rest bar parlour. Did Mulliner tell you the story of the enterprise?'

'Several times.'

'I doubt that you heard the authentic version. Mulliner, although an excellent fellow in all respects, veers, if he has a fault, towards nepotism. He may have given you the impression that the credit or blame for the Leisure Complex belongs to his nephew Auberon.'

'That is certainly what he volunteered to a small company consisting of myself, a Small Bass, a Gin and Italian Vermouth and a Thoughtful Pint of Bitter,' said the Scotch-and-soda.

'Whereas,' proceeded the Oldest Member, 'the blame or credit for the Leisure Complex may more properly be laid at the door of a quartet of spavined golfers known as the Wrecking Crew. Have I told you about the Wrecking Crew?'

'Yes,' affirmed the Scotch-and-soda with vigour.

'What I may not have told you about the Wrecking Crew was that one of their number was an architect, a second was a chartered surveyor, a third was a town clerk and a fourth was a county councillor who had the ear of a junior minister who, although otherwise blemishless, could no more handle a mashie on the short fifteenth than a six-month-old baby can dance the foxtrot. Came the day of the Visitors' Challenge Cup—'

'I do not wish to interrupt your discourse,' said the Scotch-and-soda firmly, 'but I have an important luncheon engagement and I think you have made your point. You wish to illustrate, do you not, that golf is no longer so much a sport of recreation as an alfresco version of the taint of vice whose strong corruption inhabits our frail blood? *Twelfth Night*, for your information, III, *ii*.'

'Never mind all about *Twelfth Night*, III, *ii*,' retorted the Sage with some asperity. 'If I may make so bold, you have a lot to say for yourself for a Scotch-and-soda who is only supposed to be an extra walk-on or spear-carrier. Your role, I am sorry to have to remind you is merely to provide the feed-lines to lead into my story.'

The Scotch-and-soda blanched visibly.

'What story?'

'The story I am about to tell you,' said the Oldest Member smoothly, 'of Cuthbert Dalrymple, Hermione Ironside, the Town clerk of Salterton-on-Sea, the Borough Architect of the same bracing resort, the chairman and managing director of Seaview Bungalows (Exploitation) Ltd, and a carbuncle on the body politic rejoicing in the alias of Augustus Merryweather.

'This saga of bribery and corruption in high places (continued the oldest Member, settling back in his chair) begins with a niblick tossed into the twelfth-hole bunker at the Salterton-on-Sea municipal golf-course . . .'

'I am sorry,' said the Scotch-and-soda, 'but I believe I heard the unmistakable sound of a mini-cab waiting to convey me back to the Angler's Rest. Perhaps you will continue this interesting story another time.'

The Sage pinned his reluctant guest's arm with a grip that had warped many a putter in more halcyon, innocent days.

'What,' asked the Oldest Member, is it worth?'

Trial Offer

The much praised London Small Claims Court may soon be back in business with commercial sponsorship . . . from Reader's Digest.

Guardian

Summing up, the chairman said that the Court had heard an uplifting case. It had all the elements that went towards making this crazy country of ours a bulwark against communism and a bastion of free picturesque speech: pathos, humour, warmth, compassion, dignity, understanding, religion, love of family, free enterprise, terminal illness and a dog with a broken paw.

All who had listened to the evidence would want to count their blessings. There could be few present, however laden with academic honours or steeped in knowledge gleaned from dusty books, who had not learned something about the human condition from the simple values and homely wisdom displayed by every witness without exception, from the grizzled country storekeeper with his fund of wisecracks to the eminent writer politician with his timely warnings about Soviet Russia's back door threat to democracy. The chairman himself had certainly learned something today. He had learned twelve ways to switch off tension.

Tension: that was the one state of mind you should never ask a neurotic man to snap out of.

The chairman said that the background to the case had unfolded a tale of iron discipline, unflinching courage and winsomeness that revealed new insights into one of medicine's great mysteries: the awesomely intricate blood-corpuscle 'red alert' system which defends our bodies against disease and extremist politics and which then, splintering into millions of tiny anecdotes, goes on to reproduce itself in thirty-two countries and thirteen languages. It was a long story but the chairman would condense it.

The Court had been told that on the morning of 14 September 1978, while having his regular shave in the only barbershop in Blossomville, a small clapboard town of fruit growers and apple packers in the Candyfloss Mountains, West Virginia, Arthur Withers felt a sharp pain in his right foot.

Putting the twinge down to imminent necrosis of

the short plantar ligament or a dropped razor, Arthur thought no more about it until he stopped by at his doctor's office later that same hour.

As well as being a brilliant neighbourhood limb specialist, Doc Pearson was an old golfing buddie and fishing companion who knew he could give it to his fellow-Rotarian straight from the shoulder. Arthur was suffering the early symptoms of Footloose Disease a rare and always fatal condition which causes the feet, and then the ankles, knees, wrists and elbows to fall off one by one.

The Court would have heard that Arthur nodded slowly. 'Level with me, Doc. How long have I got?'

'Maybe six months, Arthur, maybe a year. If you keep the foot active, maybe a little longer.'

'And you say there's nothing anyone can do?'

'Arthur, I said there's nothing medical science can do. There's something I can do and there's something you can do. So long as we have a pair of knees each, or three knees between the two of us, we can pray. And maybe this chart of hopping exercises will help.'

The chairman said that until he walked into Doc Pearson's office that fine September morning, Arthur Withers was a man who thought he had everything. He had fine neighbours, many fine friends, and a fine business, the Blossomville Fine Fruit Corporation. By cleverly merchandizing individually crated apples for school children all along the Eastern seaboard to take to their teachers he had accumulated his first million dollars. He was planning to give his family a vacation in Europe, and the next Fall his eldest boy would be quitting home to go to Princeton. Life had seemed good.

Did the court not agree, by the way, that there was nothing so untidy as a boy's room when he was around the house, and nothing so empty as when he'd gone?

It was not until he heard that his extremities were

about to drop off that Arthur realized there was something missing in his life. What it was he had no idea – but he knew he had to find it before it was too late. The chairman said that he had been reminded, when Arthur was giving evidence on this point, of the Spirit of Plenty which had visited three men and asked them what they wanted. The first man, a millionaire, had said, 'I want for nothing.' The second, a merchant, had said, 'I want everything I can get.' The chairman said he was hanged if he could remember what the third man, a pauper, had said, and it was not relevant to the case; but it had been such a brilliantly humble answer that the pauper had never looked back.

The Court had heard how that night Arthur Withers pondered on what he had to do. Always a practical man, full of sturdy common sense, he came up with a practical solution. He had to leave Blossom-ville, he knew that, for what he sought lay far beyond the Candyfloss Mountains. Doc Pearson had advised hopping exercises. Very well, he would hop. By jingo, he would hop further than any frog. He had promised his family a vacation in Europe. Very well, they would go to Europe, and God willing he would be there to meet them. For Arthur Withers had made up his mind to hop overland to Paris. Maybe that way he would find what he was looking for.

Arthur's incredible journey up through the United States and Canada, his nightmare trek across Siberia, his months in a Turkish jail, his comical misunder-standing with the Albanian customs officials, and his touching friendship with Rusty, the mongrel that followed him most of the way, would provide material for a dozen *Book Choices*. So far as the case under review was concerned, however, it was sufficient to say that he made a second million dollars in Athens by providing the Greeks with something they didn't already have, namely an efficient mini-cab service, that by combining faith, positive thinking and a new

134

system of deep-breathing exercises he conquered Footloose Disease and made a third million dollars from the sales of a best-selling book, *Your Limbs Don't Have To Drop Off*, that he was reunited with his family in Paris, and that in December of last year, when they had temporarily taken up residence in Eaton Square, he called in at the Pimlico workshop of George Popplewell, shoemender and saddle repair specialist, to have his boot resoled.

Arthur had sworn on oath although the boot on which he had hopped many thousands of miles had a hole in it, the other one was almost as new. The only reason he had handed them over to George Popplewell as a pair was that he had tied them together by the laces and could not unfasten the knot. He had not asked George to resole both boots, did not expect him to resole both boots, and was both surprised and annoyed when both boots came back resoled, with a bill for £4.80 which he was obliged to pay before they were released to him. He was claiming the sum of £2.40 for unnecessary soling of the nearly-new boot.

So much for Arthur's evidence. The court had heard George's side of the story. He too had a fascinating tale to tell. Four years ago he had been a respected merchant banker with all the outward trappings of success. Wealth, position, a good address, an excellent wine cellar, were all his. Yet there was something lacking—

The chairman said he was interrupting his summing-up because he had just been handed a note. Intrigued by George's account to the court of how he had found real happiness by throwing up his banking activities and becoming a simple shoemaker, Arthur had just been talking to him in the corridor and was now convinced that at long last he had stumbled across what he had spent all these months looking for. He intended to go into partnership with George, financing their joint true happiness by floating a

135

nationwide chain of simple shoemending franchises and perhaps writing a best-seller about how he made five million dollars out of being the happiest man alive. In the circumstances, he was prepared to withdraw the claim for £2.40.

Granting leave for the case to be withdrawn, the chairman said that some folk spent their whole lives looking for the crock of gold at the end of the rainbow, while others – why, they spent their whole lives working hard to earn that crock of gold, and lo and behold, there was the beginning of the rainbow.

This Summer Breed

The hum of the dragonflies was lost in the insidious drome of a distant engine. In all the back gardens of Laburnam Villas, racing pigeons cooed uneasily in sheds made out of old doors and lino.

Bert Dobbs straightened his aching back, knocked out his pipe, patted his dog, folded his copy of *Popular Gardening*, pushed back his cap, wiped bottled beer from his lips with the back of his hand, placed his thumbs inside his worn belt, and said, peering through the Sunday afternoon heat-haze:

'One of ours, gel.'

'That two-stroke Hovermower at No. 23,' said Lil Dobbs through a mouthful of clothes-pegs. 'Morning, noon and night it's going, all day and every day, come rain or shine, and there ain't nothing nor nobody can stop it.'

'Makes you proud,' said Bert.

'I wouldn't care,' said Lil, 'but they don't even have a lawn.'

'You don't understand, Lil. Do you really think a

little thing like having a backyard made of concrete is going to stop No. 23 using their Hovermower? They're made of better stuff than that, my gel. So are all of us – you, me, the people at No. 17, Fred, Queenie, Alf, the milkman, the postman . . . Little people. Ordinary people. We may not have much, and I expect we don't amount to a row of beans with bank managers and such, but don't let nobody fool you – at the end of the day we can take all the knocks what comes. It's a little thing called keeping your pecker up, and don't you forget it . . . Listen!'

'Throttle cut out, sounds like,' said Lil, looking across the gardens at the wisp of smoke rising from No. 23's Hovermower.

'Poor blighters,' said Bert.

The slap of braces on vest from the other side of the fence told Bert Dobbs that his friend and neighbour Alf Nobbs had arisen from his afternoon nap and ventured out into the sunshine to blanch his leeks.

Alf took a Woodbine stub from behind his ear, lit it, coughed, released a racing pigeon, chased the cat out of the cucumber frame, snapped off a dead lupin, belched, spat, and said:

'Wotcher, Bert.'

'Wotcher, Alf.'

'Acacia Avenue copped it last night.'

'You don't say.'

'A right packet. Roses, violets, border carnations, foxgloves, sweet williams, early-flowering chrysanths, the lot. Greenfly, story I heard.'

'Wicked, ' said Lil.

'Acacia Avenue can take it,' said Bert gruffly.

'It'll be our turn next,' warned Lil.

'And so can we, gel, if that greenfly's got our number on it. What kind of people do they think we are? I was just saying to Lil, Alf, before you come out, we may not have much, and I expect we don't amount to a row of beans with—'

'Yes, I heard you from the toilet,' said Alf hastily.
'It's a pity the old *Evening News* isn't still going, Bert.
You could have sent that up as My Best Cockney
Letter. They'd have paid you two quid for that.'

'Them was the days, Alf. Salt of the earth, them
days was.'

'They've broken the mould, Bert.'

'Talking of the old *Evening News*, Alf, did you ever tell
Lil that Best Maincrop Carrots Story you sent up?'

'I think he did,' said Lil.

'Tell Lil your Best Maincrop Carrots Story.'

'Don't know as I can remember it, Bert.'

'He's being modest, Lil. Just sown your maincrop
carrots, hadn't you, Alf?' prompted Bert.

'That April we had all the rain, it was, Lil. I'll never
forget it. I'd just sown my maincrop carrots in drills
about half inch deep and a foot apart, same as what I
always do. Stump-rooted variety they was. Nothing
special, but they meant something to me and Queenie.'

138

'Course they did,' said Bert.

'They would do,' said Lil.

'Next thing, Queenie calls me in for my dinner. No sooner had I put a knifeful of steak-and-kidney pud in my mouth than Queenie says, "I think you should go out in the garden again," she says. Just like that. In this funny voice. "I think you should go out in the garden again."'

'Woman's instinct,' said Lil.

'I said, "Arf a mo, gel, I've only just come in." She says "I know you have," she says, "but there's a blackbird pecking at your seeds." There was, too. Gawd knows where them carrots would have been if Queenie hadn't spotted it.'

'Ask him what he did, Lil,' said Bert.

'What did you do, Alf?'

'Chased it off.'

'Chased it off, he says!' chortled Bert with affectionate derision. 'You forget, Alf, I was there! He not only chased it off, Lil, he took a broom to it and ran down the garden shouting "Shoo! Shoo!"'

'Couldn't have no upstart blackbird taking liberties with my maincrop carrots,' said Alf modestly.

'See, Lil,' said Bert, contentedly lighting his pipe. 'That's what – puff – foreigners – puff – don't understand about us British. Oh, we're very easygoing up to a point, but we can only be pushed so far, and when we get our dander up – puff – watch out! Ain't that right, Alf?'

'Same as when we had that drought,' Alf said. 'We could have given in there and then. Sod it, we could have said, excuse my language, Lil, what's the use of bothering, we could have said. Ah, but what *did* we say, Bert?'

'What did we say? What did we say? After the council comes round, he means Lil. We said, "Right," we said, "if we're not allowed to use hosepipes, we'll use watering-cans. And if they stop us using watering-cans, we'll manage with teapots. And if they stop us using teapots—"'

'Yes, I remember very well what you said, Bert Dobbs!' said Lil primly.

'Seems funny now, but it wasn't funny at the time, was it, Alf?'

'It was us or them, Bert, that was the size of it.'

'That was when No. 35's fruit trees bought it, wasn't it? Pear scab.'

'S'right. Brings a lump to your throat, it does.'

'Finest gardeners what ever walked the earth, them at No. 35 was,' mused Bert.

'What was their name again, Lil?'

'Miniver, wasn't it?' said Lil.

Bert's face contorted with scorn as he spat contemptuously. 'Miniver? Course it wasn't bleeding Miniver! Bleeding landed gentry, the Minivers was! It's common people I'm taking· about, gel! Little, humble people! This happy breed! The kind of decent, ordinary, law-abiding folk what's got the guts to set about a titchy little pocket-handkerchief garden full of stones and slugs and plant out row after row of seedlings, just to show that they and us and millions like us have got what it takes to do our bit when we've got our backs to the wall. Eh, Alf? Now what was their bleeding name?'

'Muggins,' said Alf.

'Not Muggins, Alf – Huggins. There was Pa Huggins, there was Ma Huggins, there was Grandma Huggins, there was Henery Huggins, there was Ethel Huggins, there was the twins, and there was the brother-in-law. Proper cross-section, they was. What happened to them after their fruit trees copped it?'

'Put in for an allotment, didn't they?' said Alf.

Bert took off his cap and scratched his head in admiration. 'Don't that just go to show what we're made of? They knocks us down and we picks ourselves up and dusts ourselves off and starts all over again.

That's true British grit, that is.'

'Brings a lump to your throat,' said Alf.

'Makes you proud.'

'Salt of the earth.'

'Reminds me, Alf,' said Lil, pegging out the last of her washing. 'You heard from your Len lately?'

Alf stiffened. 'Who?'

'Your son Len. Lives out Sydenham way, don't he?'

'I have no son called Len,' said Alf woodenly

'Oh, Alf! he's never—?'

'Excuse me, Lil. I think I hear the kettle whistling.' With which Alf stalked indoors.

Bert mopped his brow. 'Put your foot in it there, Lil. Didn't you know they don't talk about Len no more? Evicted by the council for refusing to weed his window boxes.'

'Poor lad.'

'Poor lad nothing. It's them what's got to fight the weeds in his place you should be feeling sorry for. The incoming tenants. Dandelions up to here, by all accounts.'

Lil sighed as she picked up her empty clothes-basket.

'All the same, Bert, it makes me glad we haven't got kids of our own.'

'If we had, gel,' said Bert fiercely, 'they'd be out here helping their old dad lift these autumn-sown onions and be proud to do it. Same as what I am.'

'Oh, Bert, you're crying!'

'Get on with you, woman! It's these blooming onions.'

Just What They Wanted

The season of Xmas consist of some good things and, some bad things.

The good things are well-known to all and sundry, including many sweets and much chocolate, Money Orders from your uncle, many Parcels, etc, etc, also Xmas cake in larder, once it has been cut they cannot tell when a person has had a Slice.

The bad things consist of, namely, mistletoe, opening Parcels when it is only a new pullover, going to church, and, having to give Presents to all your parents.

The latter not fair. They, your parents, only have to give Presents to one of you, but you, yourself, have to give Presents to two of them, as well as to, your Granny. If you do not, your Father rant and rave, exclaiming at the same time in tones of Great Bitterness (He no consideration for anyone but himself. Very well two can play at game, just wait till his birthday, he will get Nothing.)

For their Presents, you can either Make them things or, you can Buy them things. Of these, it best to Buy them things, as you do not have to use Glue.

To buy Presents, first you must have some Money. Strange to relate, this easiest part, it is easy also peasy. The person just say to their Mother (I do not have any

Money). NB, Do not say this to your Father. After the person's Mother have said (Why you not have money, I thought you were supposed to be Saving Up, we been telling you since last August to stop frittering away your pocket money on Rubbish), she will give that person some Money, adding for good measure, (Do not tell your Father or he will go Mad). NB, Do not say (He mad already).

When you have got Money, you should not spend it on yourself as, your Mother will go Mad and tell your Father, then he go Purple, saying (It your own fault, you spoil that boy Rotten), then she go Sad and cry, saying, (I just not seem to be able to get Through to him). Instead of spending the Money on yourself, you should get Their Presents with commendable speed, so that when you have Got them you will see how much got left. This the person can spend on What He Likes.

The person has to Choose the Presents yourself, it no use asking them what want. If you ask them (What want Xmas?) they will aver sturdily, (Nothing), but, they do not mean it. If you keep on asking (What want Xmas?) to your Father, that Testy individual will explode in no uncertain manner (For heaven sake, lad, if you can not summon up the effort and imagination to buy Xmas presents without being told what get, there no point in bothering at all), but, he still does not mean it. If, you do not get him One, that person's Father will get his Own Back.

Although they will not vouchsafe genially what want Xmas, people's Mothers and their Father always volunteer grimly what each other not want Xmas. Your Mother always say, (do not buy your Father another key-ring, there a dear, he cannot get in his Dressing-table Drawer for key rings) also, (And he not really have a sweet tooth, if you thinking of buying anything chocolatey). Meanwhile, That Worthy issue the Stark Warning, (Whatever get for your

Mother for God sake do not give her a cheap Diary, she like to choose her own.) This not true, if you give your Mother a Diary she will assert gleefully as sure as night follow day, (Oh, a Diary. How lovely darling.)

But, the best thing to give your Mother is, some soap. This is because, Mothers are always Washing. But, you are supposed to buy it, even though as well as Soap you have also Made her a Diary, this can be done by cutting a notebook in two and carefully copying out the dates for this year Diary. If they, your Mother, think you not buy it, the Soap, they pout in injured tones, (Oh really darling, this not really present. Anyone can go into bathroom and wrap up piece of Soap.) Your Father snarl through gritted teeth, (It not even a New tablet, it still Wet. You selfish little Monkey, what done with all that money you were given to buy Presents?) For this reason, you should give them Soap in the shape of Snoopy, then they cannot say, that you have got it out of the Bathroom, as, they cannot remember if the Snoopy Soap you gave them for her Birthday is still in, the Soap Jar. She will then cry blissfully, (Oh, Soap.)

As well as Soap, Mothers also like bath salts, chocolate mints, a pen, a jewelled cigarette-holder, comb and combcase, spare Kleenex holder, pkt of safety-pins, or, a shoe-horn. Each of these gifts will be received with Transports of Delight. They will say (Oh, a pkt of safety-pins), or, if not know what is, (Oh, what is?)

The worst thing give your Mother is, some Scent. It all right When Everybody Else give them Scent, but, when you give her scent, it not all right, even though, you have spent a lot of Money on a Big Bottle of the same. It Your Father not like it, not your Mother. She, your Mother, sniff at the latter exclaiming, (Oh, scent), but, Your Father make face as if it Dog dirt, exclaiming, (Pooh, what a pong, what it called, Eau de Ballspond Road?) Whereupon, she your Mother, ejaculate stoutly:

(It very sweet of him, thank you darling). But, strange to relate, she will never wear the Scent from that day to this, as Your Father will not let her. This because he is jealous, because, the person has bought their Mother scent, but, my Father has only brought her a brooch.

While on the subject of such Strange Bedfellows, the best thing to give Your Father for Xmas is, a big cigar. These are proper cigars but, you can only buy them in Souvenir shops. They twelve inches long. The person's Father will chuckle with many a hearty smile. .(My goodness me, that a cigar and a half and no mistake, thank you my boy I take it to the office and smoke it there). If he not smoke, a key-ring make a useful present, even if he have one already you can get different ones and, he can collect them, as, his Hobby.

As well as cigars and another Key-ring, Fathers also like six boxes of matches with, pictures of old cars on them, a novelty bottle-opener, tin of shortbread, new plant pot, or, some more handkerchieves, and, an address book, this can be made from other half of notebook which, the person used to Make her Diary, by merely cutting Index tabs on the pages, then, lettering each one carefully, A, B, C, E, etc, etc.

The worst thing give Your Father is, flowers. Even though they grow them in their garden, they do not like them. He say (What this? Some kind of practical joke?) quickly followed by, the murmured aside, (I seriously think that boy not all there). It he who not all there.

This leave only your Granny. You can give them anything, NB bar of butterscotch, pencil sharpener shaped like golfball, pr of nail-scissors, pkt of carbon paper etc, etc, and they will chortle heartily, (My my, just what wanted). Even when your Father remarks curtly (What earth does he imagine his Grandmother want with a shaving mirror?) the Faithful Old Soul will riposte with a merry twinkle, (It the thought that counts). If, you do not have any Money left, you can cut up some Brown Paper and make them a Photograph Album. If they were your Father, they would throw it away, but, if they are Your Granny, they will keep it.

Last, but, not least, the Things you buy have to be Wrapped up in a Parcel, you cannot just give them them saying (Merry Xmas). But, you do not have to buy our own wrapping paper, you can use theirs. But, if you have bought your Father flowers, and it is too late to take them back, these should not be wrapped Up in a Parcel.

Here Comes the Crowd!

. . . waiting, as I said, for the last of the 2700 guests to arrive before members of the Royal Family, accompanied by an escort of the Household Cavalry, take their places here in St Paul's with its royal association going back as far as Ethelred, King of Kent in the seventh century, although there has not been a royal wedding here since the marriage on 14 November 1501, of Arthur, elder son of Henry VII, to—

But here, magnificent in his ultramarine and mustard-yellow heraldic robes with his vermilion sash of the Order of St Cuthbert and carrying his ostrich-plumed velvet tricorne, is the imposing – six foot one and a half, to be exact – figure of Sir Penrose Molyneux Folyneux, hereditary Adroit Privy King of Arms, traditional Keeper of the Queen's Beehives which are here symbolically represented by the silver honey-pot carried on a brocaded cushion of swansdown by Adroit Privy's personal page, the eleven-year-old Master Rupert Damn.

I must apologize for that slight hiccup there, having just had the bad luck to drop all my notes off the edge of

146

the commentators' balcony. Order of service, list of guests, background material, the lot, have all gone fluttering down into the choir and I'm wondering now if there's any chance of getting them back.

And I've just been told there's not a cat in hell's chance of getting those essential papers back until after the wedding and we must soldier on as best we can. So much for doing one's homework.

A slight lull now as Adroit Privy King of Arms takes his place alongside I think Chester Herald. Chester Herald looking very colourful in his colourful robes. And Adroit Privy King of Arms next to him.

No sign yet of the few remaining guests still to come. Perhaps the traffic lights at Ludgate Circus are against them. I know that when we drove along the royal route very early this morning, the traffic lights at Ludgate Circus were very slow to change, so perhaps that's the reason for the hold-up.

This magnificent cathedral, built of course by Sir Christopher Wren after the other cathedral, its predecessor, burned down in the Great Fire of London. Whereupon, so the story goes, Sir Christopher Wren promptly built this great Cathedral, the one we're in now, with its famous Whispering Gallery which tourists come from all over the world to—

And my colleague has just passed me a note to say that whatever the reason for the delay it can't be the traffic lights at Ludgate Circus which in fact would have been switched off by now to enable the magnificent Royal Wedding procession to come through unimpeded. Presumably the magnificent royal coach will be waved on by a policeman on point duty.

The organist playing the organ now, and this piece was specially selected by the Master of the Queen's Musick for today's impressive ceremony. That's musick spelt with a 'k' for the uninitiated, this being a very ancient office even older I believe than that of Adroit Privy King of Arms. And the organ music that the

147

organist is playing so I've been told is one of His Royal Highness's favourite organ—

And here come the last of the guests before the arrival of the Royal Family resplendent in their magnificent regalia. Cheered by a crowd numbering thousands who've been waiting since dawn here today, they've been waved on at Ludgate Circus by the traffic policeman in his magnificent helmet and burnished medals and here they come now.

A gentleman in black knee breeches, purple sort of vest thing and clerical collar, clearly the last of the many bishops who've assembled here this morning for this right royal occasion. The bishop's wife next to him in her blue coat, and as they take their seats, other guests following them through the Big West Door of Wren's masterpiece, this crowning achievement of the man of whom it was rightly said, 'If you want to see his monument, look around you.' And here comes another guest, and another, and another, filing in one behind the other, several of them accompanied by their wives or husbands in blue or green or pale fawn coats, as they enter this magnificent Abbey. Cathedral.

And who's this very distinguished-looking figure in immaculate morning dress with row upon row of medal miniatures on the right lapel of his immaculate –? I do believe, yes, it's, the Duke of Edinburgh. The Duke of Edinburgh taking his place now in almost the very back row, squeezing past representatives from all over the—

I've just been informed it can't possibly be the Duke of Edinburgh, who of course will be arriving in the main magnificent procession which is probably even now making its way along the Mall, lined with cheering crowds who've been waiting since dawn to catch a glimpse of this fairy-tale wedding of the century. Along the Mall, across Trafalgar square, up not Charing Cross Road, the Strand, up the Strand with its cheering flag-waving crowds, along Fleet Street, then waved on by the magnificent policeman at Thingy Circus to continue the royal journey up that hill to the very steps of this magnificent monument to Christopher Wren, with its royal associations going back centuries.

The guests now talking quietly among themselves as they wait for the Royal Family. The new arrival mistaken by many for the Duke of Edinburgh having a word with his neighbour, a lady wearing a hat. The organist playing the organ. Many of the guests reading the Order of Service which will enable them to follow what's going on.

And now the Beefeaters are they? Somebody's told me their correct title is Yeomen of the Guard. The Yeomen of the Guard in their magnificent red and gold uniforms come to attention with their pole things and there's a fanfare of trumpets from the trumpeters of the Royal Household Trumpet Brigade which must surely mean that the royal party is—

And yes. Here they come now through the Big Door. I recognize Princess Margaret wearing pale blue clothes and jewellery. Prince Michael and his radiant wife Princess Michael, also wearing clothes and jewellery. Princess Alexandra and her husband, Prince Alexandra. Princess Anne of course is there, and several of the royal children with various names, but not it goes without saying Princess Anne's new baby who is too young to walk. The Queen Mother who is the mother of the Queen, whose own daughter correction son is to be married here by the Archbishop of, the one who's here today. And now the congregation of distinguished guests, from Adroit Privy King of Arms down to the latest new arrival, bow or curtsey as the case may be, as the Queen herself, accompanied by her husband the Duke of Edinburgh in the uniform of a duke, and followed by their attendants all brilliantly attired for this magnificent occasion, make their way up the long aisle to the front seats. Pews. The organist still playing the organ and I believe if I turn the microphone in this direction as we await the arrival of Prince Charles you should be able to hear what he's playing . . .

But now from the crowds who've been waiting since dawn outside there's a mighty burst of cheering that almost lifts the great dome of this magnificent place where we are to its very foundations, and that can only mean one thing. And here he comes now, wearing the full dress uniform of an officer, escorted by soldiers in their ceremonial clanking things, breastplates, and flanked one either side by the two brothers who are to act as his supporters, following the tradition of previous royal weddings such as many others. The two brothers being of course Prince Andrew and the other one.

And I should have mentioned there that the groom is none other than His Royal Highness the Prince of Wales.

And now everyone from Prince Andrew to Adroit Privy King of Arms eagerly awaits the arrival of the bride. And as the organist strikes up that familiar tune we've all heard so many times at weddings, here she comes along the wide space between the two rows of seats, radiant in the long dress that was specially made for her. Yes, accompanied by some little girls also in long dresses and a chap who must be her father, it's Lady no don't tell me it's on the tip of my tongue . . .

Gob Stoppers

Whether because of industrial action, or because of the BBC having to eke out its wretched remittance on repeats, or because of incomprehensible serials based on the works of John le Carré, or because of Des

150

O'Connor, television looks like relaxing its stranglehold on the nation this winter.

What then, will the nation be doing with itself during the yawning void between the cocktail hour and Closedown, apart from propagating the species, stockpiling letters to *The Times*, ferreting down the side of the sofa for missing chess pieces, and growing a moustache?

The answer is that it will be resuscitating the art of conversation.

As it is well known, conversation was just about killed off by the arrival of television, the only surviving topic for popular discussion being television itself, with especial reference to that bloody rubbish they had the nerve to put on last night. Even that once flourishing branch of the art, motoring talk, has withered and all but died. In an age of motorways, when a barked 'M5 Exit 12' passes for detailed route directions to someone's weekend cottage who wants to hear a ten-minute set-piece on the best way of getting from A to B without going through Z?

Through the long decline of what older readers will recall was a pleasant form of social intercourse, however, the vocal chords have generally remained in use, mainly for ordering drink in public houses or asking what is on the other channel. With this equipment in reasonable working order, a revival of the art of conversation should be possible. It has been so long neglected, though, that it will be necessary to get back to basics.

What conversation is
It is a verbal approximation of the game of rugby football, where one player has the ball and the other side try to get it off him.

What conversation is for
Like vanity publishing, it is a harmless method of inflating the ego. Unlike vanity publishing, it does not cost any money, since the last thing the conversationalist in full flow is going to do is interrupt himself to buy the next round of drinks.

What conversation is about
Conversation can be about anything except religion, which is a non-starter. In the old days it was usually confined to the weather or medical matters, but field-tests have indicated that the following topics would be regarded as acceptable in a more broadminded age:

Conditions at Heathrow airport;

The reluctance of American hotels to take real money;

House prices and mortgage rates;

Double glazing;

The difficulty of finding window-cleaners, in the context of the unemployment figures;

Postal delays;

The black economy, as typified by cowboy plumbers;

The genealogy of London taxi drivers;

Car thieves, coupled with the names of these friends whose grandmother died while they were halfway across Greece, so they had to put her in the boot;

Irish affairs.

How to start a conversation

A quorum (ie, one other player) being present, the conversationalist should blow ostentatiously up his nostrils, at the same time observing, 'Typical', 'Doesn't it make you want to spit!', or 'Would you sodding credit it!' Although his opponent(s) will see the trap yawning ahead, there is an obligation upon the opposition to ask, 'What?' Whereupon, waving his newspaper – but on no account allowing the other side to read it – the conversationalist should briefly state his theme, eg 'This Maltese chef', 'Bloody town hall bureaucrats', or 'Flaming building societies.'

Note the cryptic nature of these gambits. By over-elaborating, ie, 'Bloody Maltese chef, tries to make a crème caramel with HP sauce, gets fired, and blow me if the Industrial Tribunal don't reinstate him!', the conversationalist would be extending an open invitation to other players to seize command with something on the lines of, 'Oh, you ain't heard nothin' yet, as Al Jolson used to say. What about the petrol pump attendant who was sacked for persistent arson? Now it so happens my brother knows that case from the inside . . .'

Even the ambiguous opening shot has its perils, for it is not uncommon for other contenders to retaliate at once with, 'Don't talk to me about building societies, I'm up to here with them,' or 'Town hall bureaucrats? Have I told you the latest on my planning permission saga?' What the conversationalist must do is discard his lead the moment he has played it, launching without delay into a story or series of connected recollections that the others cannot easily interrupt: 'This Maltese chef. Reminds me of one year we thought we'd try Tenerife, it was total and absolute disaster from start to finish . . .'

How to take over a conversation
In the event of a conversation being already in progress when the conversationalist arrives in the playing area, he should watch for the speaker drawing breath and then interject: 'Same as a friend of mine, only in his case he was coming back from Marbella . . .'

It is not necessary to wait for the end of the story, or even of the sentence, before interrupting.

Having seized the initiative, however, the conversationalist must not assume that the deposed speaker has necessarily relinquished his position for good. Should he chime in with an echo effect at the end of sentences ('. . . hotel, yerss', '. . . stomach-pump, mm', '. . . British consulate, quite') it is a sure sign that he is looking for an opportunity to make a comeback with,'. . . damages, exactly. But if I can just very quickly finish my story . . .'

Hints for speakers
When engaged in conversation, never put anything in question form, whether rhetorical or otherwise. To ask, 'That restaurant in Throttle Alley, what's it bloody called again, used to be a sawdust mill?' is to invite a takeover bid from someone who knows that its name is Chompers, was present at its opening night when it showed promise, used to eat there regularly until the prices started to go through the ceiling, finally told them to go and stuff themselves when he had that punch-up with the head waiter which he'll tell you about in a minute, and now uses a place that's just opened up in the same street curiously enough, used to be a heel bar, absolutely charming but you've got to

book because there's only one table . . .'

Never generalize. One specific illustration of an item of first class mail taking three and a half weeks to get from Paddington to Notting Hill is worth twenty minutes' invective against the Post Office. Beware, however, of the capping ploy, whereby other speakers will vie to give better examples.

Direct argument is frowned upon in conversation. If you do not agree with a speaker's contention that the cross-Channel ferry is making us the laughing-stock of the world, do not contradict him but simply go on repeating, 'I had the opposite experience. I had the opposite experience. I had the opposite experience,' until you have the floor. (The phrase 'Speak as you find' may also be employed in this context.)

It is not etiquette, either, to call another conversationalist a liar or to make snide remarks suggesting that the truth and he are strangers. Should an opponent relate how a friend of his found eight human fingertips in his car boot after disturbing thieves and driving away at speed, do not sneer that this is very funny indeed because the last time you heard that story it wasn't a Cortina, it was an Austin Allegro, and it wasn't eight fingertips, it was four. All that is required of you is to say that talking of car-thieves, these friends of yours were touring Greece with their grandmother who was ninety-seven . . .

There's a Lot of Calls for It

The Swiss telephone authorities have set up a special number for obscene phone calls.

News item

How to get the best from your obscene phone call: The Obscene Calls Service is for subscribers who wish to make calls of a filthy, depraved, disgusting or perverted

155

nature. It is NOT a complaints service. If, for example, a traffic warden has wrongly given you a ticket and you wish to threaten to saw her head off, you should ring the appropriate department of the Metropolitan Police (listed in your directory). But if you wish to strap the traffic warden to the bonnet of your car and have sexual congress with her, dial the Obscene Calls Service.

The Obscene Calls Service cannot pass on messages to nymphomaniacs. However, it will certainly pretend to do so if you find it stimulating.

The Obscene Calls Service cannot trace women who pose naked at bathroom windows. Ring Directory Enquiries (142) for this service.

Before you make your call: Obscene phone pests are prone to a form of psychological hypothermia caused by nervous shivering and the fact that they are very often minus their trousers. If you are calling from home make sure the room temperature is above 24 Centigrade (about 75° Fahrenheit) and the blinds are drawn. If you are in a public call-box you should keep your mackintosh tightly buttoned.

To dial the Obscene Calls Service: Lift the receiver. Take a deep breath or series of deep breaths to control your pulse rate, and dial the correct number with your finger. If your hands are shaking, use a pencil. Do not use anything else as this may upset the delicate mechanism of your apparatus.

The correct number to dial is 998. If in your excitement, your finger (or pencil) slips on the last digit, and a voice answers 'Emergency. Which service do you require, please?' *hang up*. It is an offence to tell the emergency operator that you want the full relief massage service.

The ringing tone for the Obscene Calls Service is a series of rhythmic aspirate sounds, ie, 'hhhhh *hhhhh* hhhhh *hhhh*'. If the ringing tone is the conventional repeated burr-burr, you have dialled the wrong number. It is an offence to make obscene calls to a wrong number.

In case of difficulty ring the Supervisor (191) and tell her that you want the Obscene Calls Service. Do not tell the Surpervisor that you want her body.

NB: 'Difficulty' means difficulty in placing your call. It does not mean any other difficulties you may have, which the Supervisor will not wish to discuss with you.

When your call is answered: So that conditions for your obscene call may be as authentic as possible, the only announcement you will hear from the Obscene Calls Operator will be a nervous, guarded, 'Hello?' You should then breathe in sharply and audibly, with your mouth close to the receiver. When you hear the

Operator say, ostensibly to a friend, 'Oh God, it's another one of those,' you may begin your obscene call.

Be brief. Remember that other pests wish to make use of the limited lines available, so you are asked to bring your obscene phone call to an end within three minutes.

The operator will give you a series of verbal time checks. *After the first minute* she will say, 'Look, I don't know who you are or what you want but I honestly think you should see a doctor.' *After the second minute* she will say, 'I hope you know these calls can be traced nowadays.' *After the third minute*, affecting to speak to Scotland Yard on another telephone, she will say, 'Yes, officer, I've got him on the other line. I'll keep him talking, shall I?' This is the signal that it is now the time to replace your receiver.

Do not pester the operator. The operators are not permitted to tell you what kind of underwear they have on, if any, so asking intimate questions is a waste of valuable time. (See *Making Your Call*.) However, it may help you to know that none of the operators on the Obscene Calls Service can be satisfied except by a football team and that they are all fond of bondage games. On one evening a week they man the switchboard naked except for black stockings.

Making Your Call. Unless you are a naturally fluent speaker you should have some idea of what you are going to say before you make your obscene call. It may help to make notes, so long as you destroy them afterwards. Do not flounder and do not stray from the point.

This is the *wrong way* to make an obscene call: 'Er, hello. Er, you don't know me but, er, I've been told, er, by some of my friends, er, that, er, you like, er, a good time. Well, er, *I* like a good time, and, er, it just so happens that I'm sitting here, like, er, you know, (*inaudible*) and I was wondering if, er, you'd like me to (*inaudible*).'

This is the *right* way to make an obscene call: 'This is Eric of Hendon and I'm a first-time caller. I am wearing nothing but socks. I have got a big one. I bet you do not wear knickers. I would like to cover you all over with Golden Syrup and have you from now until Christmas. I bet you would enjoy it.'

Whispering. If you wish to whisper your obscene call, the most effective and hygienic way is to place a handkerchief over the mouthpiece. If you do not have a handkerchief, and you are speaking from a public call-box, please use your sleeve to remove traces of spittle from the mouthpiece when you have finished your call.

Heavy breathing. Some pests wish to make breathing noises instead of articulating their hopes and dreams in four-letter words. You would be helping the Obscene Calls Service run more efficiently if, instead of wasting the operator's time by breathing at her, you would ask – in an audible whisper – for the heavy Breathing Apparatus. She will then connect you with an answering machine which will record your breathing.

To breathe effectively into a telephone receiver you should hold the mouthpiece four inches away from your face and inhale and exhale in alternate gasps from the back of the throat, increasing the rhythm of the cycle gradually. Do not try to make breathing noises while smoking.

Young boys. At present, due to staffing shortages, the Obscene Calls Service has no male operators. However, by asking your operator for 'Rough Trade' you may be connected with the Obscene Calls Supervisor, who has a deep voice.

Complaints. You can also ask to be connected with the Supervisor if you have a complaint against the Obscene Calls Service – for example, if the Operator laughs at you or says she bets you couldn't do it even if she turned up at your door with a mattress strapped to her back. You may tell the Supervisor that your Operator is frigid, but you must not cry or try to discuss the youthful trauma you once had with a hooker.

The Obscene Callers' National Council is an independent statutory body set up under the Post Office Act 1969 to represent the interests of obscene callers using Post Office Services. It will listen to any suggestions you have to make about improving the Obscene Calls Service, or any complaints you may have after the Supervisor has told you to stop snivelling and buy yourself an inflatable doll. The address of the Obscene Callers' National Council is in your Blue Pages.

Motel Paradiso

'Crossroads', the long-running ITV soap-opera, moved into a cul-de-sac yesterday, when the man who directs its path made clear the time has come for something new . . . He confessed plans were in hand to find a new soap-opera . . . Pilot scripts have already been commissioned.

Guardian

The series so far:
Tycoon Ralph Smethwick, together with his alcoholic wife Mona, his sex-obsessed daughter Tina, his mentally-deranged stepdaughter Margaret, his reliable son Gareth, his unreliable son Andrew, his kleptomaniac mother Helen Solihull (she married again, having stolen her best friend's husband), his sharp-tongued but soft-hearted housekeeper Mrs Hands-

worth, and his mystery-man chauffeur Stechford, has moved into the charming but fire-prone Black Country mansion Green Acres, partly because it has twin turrets in which his half-witted stepdaughter and light-fingered mother may be locked away whenever they need to be written out of an episode, but mainly so that Ralph can be in the same series as his neurotic mistress Gail, who dare not leave the nearby motor-way-threatened cottage she shares with her insanely-jealous unsuccessful actor husband Donald Sellyoak because of the blackmailing hold he has over her gay illegimate son Chris. But there is just one snag . . .

In rushing to become the owner of Green Acres (against the advice of handsome, too-smooth-by-half lawyer Simon Edgbaston that the leasehold has not yet been checked by the copyright department), Ralph has unwittingly crossed the path of industrial chemist Greg Sutton-Coldfield, whose brutal tossing aside like a worn-out glove of his one-time fiancée Mona Smethwick was what had turned her to the gin bottle, so frustrated was she that the most dramatic scene of her career was over and done with before the series had even started. Sutton-Coldfield had himself wished to buy Green Acres, his purpose being to exploit the rich noxious substance deposits on which he believes the mansion's foundations are sunk. Knowing that per-mission for a demolition order would never be granted by Mr R. G. Bullring, bureaucratic chairman of the local planning committee, he was intending to absent himself to another production while his side-kick Arthur Sparkbrook burned Green Acres down. Frus-trated by Smethwick, however, he must wait until it is time for either the crazy stepdaughter or the klepto-maniac mother to be written out of the series, when a tipped-over candle in either the east or west turret will do the job for him. Meanwhile, after Smethwick flatly refuses even to grant him sludge-quarrying rights in the deer paddock, Sutton-Coldfield plans his revenge, little knowing that his unforgiving ex-mistress Mona Smethwick (he had known her only by her stage name, Joyce Castle Bromwich) is blurrily watching his every move . . .

But the fur does not really begin to fly until the return home of housekeeper Mrs Handsworth's runaway son Gerry, who has changed his name to Stourbridge so that his mother, who has failing eyesight, will not know who he is until episode ten. Believed to have drowned himself after being taunted for his impotence by the nymphomaniac Tina Smethwick, Stourbridge has in fact been on a television producer's training course, knocked about the world a bit, and come back with his head full of plans to rent a disused motel in the neighbourhood, until recently the site of a long-running soap opera, and convert it into a sitcom, at the same time taking his revenge on Tina by cruelly auditioning her for the daffy girl-friend part and then saying that he is sorry but he needs someone with more experience. Despite the warnings of the smooth-talking lawyer Simon Edgbaston that if he persists in taking over the motel he may come up against all sorts of unexpired foreign rights and summer repeats, Stourbridge goes ahead with his plan and hires what he believes to be a scatty couple and their way out son to be his main characters. (Unknown to him, however, these are in real life none other than Donald Sellyoak, whose last part was in *Jim's Inn* twenty years ago, and his wife Gail and her gay illegitimate son Chris, neither of whom has ever acted in comedy before but who Sellyoak has forced into being his accomplices by threatening to reveal to the Press the outcome of episode nineteen of their existing series, where Gail flies to meet her lover Ralph Smethwick in a light aircraft that has been tampered with by the mystery-man chauffeur Stechford. It is a tense moment when novice-pilot Gail, her fuel almost gone, runs into a fog-bank . . .)

The cat is really put among the pigeons when

Stourbridge learns that turning a soap-opera motel into a sitcom open-plan house with loft flatlet for the whacky lodger is a change of use, and that he must apply for planning permission. There is a surprise in store when he sets out to do just that. To pay out Mr R. G. Bullring for refusing to allow him to demolish Green Acres in the event of his having been successful in buying the place, Greg Sutton-Coldfield has got himself elected to the council and by falsely accusing Bullring of accepting bribes to allow the construction of a cops-and-robbers car-chase in a Green Belt, has forced him to resign and has himself become the new chairman of the local planning committee, which he has renamed the local plotting committee. Sutton-Coldfield blandly hears Stourbridge out. No, there is no reason why the disused motel should not be converted into a sitcom. Yes, Sutton Coldfield might be able to push the application through in time for the autumn schedules. No, he does not want a fat part in the show. But if Stourbridge really wants to show his gratitude, there is just one small favour he can do . . .

Sutton-Coldfield unfolds his little plan. Before the motel is equipped with two-tone doorbell and turned into the kind of crazy home where anything can happen and usually does, why not use it as a dump for dangerous chemicals? Since moving into Green Acres, Ralph Smethwick has been trying to buy a small objectionable wastes plant which he wants to turn into a discreet restaurant where the cast can discover one another having secret affairs. Unknown to Smethwick, the mysterious 'Mr Wolverhampton' who owns the factory is in reality Greg Sutton-Coldfield who has stubbornly refused to sell out of malice. Now, however, everything falls neatly into place. Sutton-Coldfield will let the sale go through at a fat profit to himself, first having shipped drums of putrid acid from the plant to the disused motel with the connivance of Gerry Stourbridge, who as well as being anxious to please Sutton-Coldfield has his own score to settle with the

163

Smethwick family. That way, when the fumes from the motel cause the surrounding populace to come out in blisters, Smethwick as new owner of the objectionable wastes plant will get the blame. Or so Sutton-Coldfield hopes . . .

But complications set in when a deputation of villagers march on Green Acres, ostensibly to complain about the fumes. Smethwick instructs Mrs Handsworth to admit a low-budget delegatioon of three, whereupon – his head full of the news he has just heard that Tina is pregnant, Mona wants a divorce and Mrs Solihull has been arrested again – he sits resignedly at his desk to listen to their grievances. But it is not as straightforward as that. Once they are squashed side by side on a sofa facing the cameras, Smethwick's three visitors reveal their true identity. 'Mrs Walsall' is in reality a viewer, who has come to express her disgust at this load of tripe replacing her favourite programme. 'Miss Bromsgrove' is a member of the Independent Broadcasting Authority, delivering a solemn warning that unless the script improves and the set designer does something to stop the drawing-room wall shaking, the series will be taken off the air. 'Stan National Exhibition Centre, Birmingham' is a small-part actor who once stopped at the Crossroads filling station for petrol. 'But for you and your interfering kind, Smethwick,' he snarls, 'I might have been built up as the latest mystery Romeo in the life of garage secretary Sharon. Well, you're not going to get away with it!'

Before anyone can utter, 'Look out, he has a gun and he means to use it!' the telephone rings. It is Edgbaston the so-suave lawyer. 'I thought you might like to know, Smethwick,' he drawls. 'I've just heard that Green Acres, as it calls itself, isn't all it seems. Not only does it turn out to be the house they're using in *Brideshead Revisited*, but it isn't even in the Midlands. You can't say I didn't warn you, old boy . . .'

Now tune in to the second thrilling instalment.

Jolly Voting Weather

Applications are being sought for the post of Head
Master of Eton following the decision of Michael
McCrum to retire next summer.

Daily Mail

Having been advised that a formal application by me
for the headmastership of Eton College is likely to be
favourably received by the governors should my
curriculum vitae prove to be satisfactory, I have pleasure
in appending the necessary details. I would first,
however, wish to stress that should your kind invitation
to submit this application turn out to be an elaborate
practical joke, the culprits will be sought out and
punished with the utmost severity.

My headed writing paper having been appropriated
by an international jewel thief and master of disguise
who for the whole of one term masqueraded as myself
while I was visiting my twin brother in New Zealand, I
will save you the trouble of turning to my signature by
vouchsafing at once that I am Septimus Smugg, MA,
and that I was until the establishment was closed down
by the inspectors from D. C. Thomson Ltd, a senior
master in the Red Circle School stories in the *Hotspur*.

I hasten to say that the School's premature closure
had no connection with any affair involving whitewash,
soot, a billygoat, a mad bull, the schoolboy with the
amazing memory and a distinguished guest of honour
who was regrettably mistaken for an intruder and tied
up with a clothes-line, which may have come to your
ears; and while it may be technically true that resulting
from this incident I was dismissed from my post in the
heat of the moment, I was reinstated in the following
episode due to the mysterious illness which confined all
the other masters to the sanatorium.

No, gentlemen: my belief is that the death-knell
sounded for Red Circle School on the day, some years
ago, that we were reduced from 10,000 closely-printed
words each week to a two-page picture story. You can

imagine, I am sure, the effect upon morale. It could not have been more damaging had we gone comprehensive. You may be sure that should this application be successful, I would fight to the death any proposal that may be in the pipeline to convert Eton College into a cartoon strip.

While touching on the reputation of what after all is a very superior scholastic institution, and with no wish to be premature, may I say that my first act upon assuming my headmagisterial duties would be to change its name to the more prestigious-sounding Eton Academy. I am well aware that this may spark off a Fourth Form Mutiny or Schoolboy Siege but no-one has more experience than the undersigned at handling undisciplined specimens who take to the chapel roof and hurl down water bombs and bags of soot. I am taking it as read that I will be furnished with a full list of the names of all boys with twin brothers, whether believed to be in Australia or not, as it is my experience that they are often the ringleaders in escapades of this kind.

I contemplate one further innovation. As you gentlemen may or may not be aware – I forget whether this information was listed in *The Public Schools Year Book*, but it was certainly to be found in *The Hotspur Annual* in my day – Red Circle School was divided into three houses: Home House (English lads only), Trans-Atlantic or, colloquially, Yank House (our American and Canadian Cousins), and Colonial or Conk House (boys from all other parts of the Empire, whether coffee-coloured or not). The formula was an exceptionally successful one, providing opportunities without number for inter-house feuds, dorm raids and other japes, infiltrating by twin brothers or outright imposers, sieges, 'sit-ins' (as one supposes the Yank House Rebellion would now be dubbed!) and other character-building activities. It would be my intention to reorganize Eton Academy upon these lines, my impression of the present arrangement being that the existence of such a very large number of houses must often lead to confusion when pranksters of one nationality or shade of skin propose to debag rotters of another. Needless to say, the nomenclature of Colonial or Conk House would have to be 'updated' to New Commonwealth or New Conk House (Arabs, for our purposes, would count as New Conks).

As to my qualifications for reorganizing the Academy on so Arnoldian a scale: whilst the accolade of a headmastership was denied me in the Red Circle stories – largely (I suspect) because of the unfortunate business of the wretched Amazing India-rubber Boy of the Remove, who with his dubious circus connections was entirely to blame for the presence of an escaped gorilla in the Conk House gymnasium at the very moment an important South African personage was being conducted into that building by myself and the Bursar, with a view to persuading him to contribute handsomely to the Sports Fund which had been sadly denuded following the visit of a bogus maharajah who had passed himself off as the uncle of Punjab Singh of Study Number Five – I nevertheless have had considerable experience as Acting Headmaster when the incumbent has been confined to his quarters with red paint-spots believed at the time to be measles, visiting his twin brother in Canada or otherwise written out of the series.

Nor, I regret to say, have I ever been a housemaster, although the sinecure has often been within my grasp. It was the fact of my own twin brother causing my embarrassment by turning up at Sports Day in a check suit and bookmaker's satchel that cost me the house-mastership of Home House, while similar appointments to Yank House and Conk House respectively were vetoed following the episodes of the dead fish in the broomcloset and the fiasco of the midnight fire drill, also respectively. Yet here again, I am able to claim that I have gained considerable experience in the responsibility of housemastership by assuming the mantle of *locum* when other masters have been suffering from loss of memory or, upon being mistaken for their ne'er-do-well twin brothers, have been imprisoned for short periods.

(Here I would interject that it would be my policy at Eton Academy to give senior masters with staring eyes every opportunity to act as new brooms, instigate reigns of terror etc, whenever any of my housemasters may be visiting the Dominions or taking leave of absence after receiving messages from mysterious Chinamen.)

To conclude this summary of my academic career: since leaving the Red Circle stories, I have been a supply teacher in various boys' annuals, story papers and comics. Since few of these publications are recognized as efficient by the Department of Education and Science, I have thought it appropriate to pursue my vocation under various assumed names. You may be sure, however, that whether being chased by a bedsheet 'ghost' at the Haunted School, walking into a whitewash-bucket booby trap at Dr Whackem's Academy, or inflicting six of the best on the Bash Street Kids, Septimus Smugg, MA, has never for a moment hung up his mortarboard, except for a brief period when, for reasons I need not touch on in this *curriculum vitae*, he was the ruler of a small island in the Southern hemisphere.

Gentlemen, it is because your priceless establishment with its top hats, tuck shops, traditions and privileges seems to belong within the pages of a boys' paper circa 1933 – a vintage academic year in my humble opinion, not least because it was the year the *Hotspur* was founded – that I apply for this position, Japesters, beware! Slackers, take heed! Malingerers, and the twin brothers of malingerers, have a care! Impostors, unwind your turbans and sponge the walnut-stain from your faces! Smugg is on his way, and time swishes to a stop.

Our Gang

The Government is considering the possibility of
reducing the qualifying age for election to public office
to 18, a Home Office Minister said yesterday. This
would mean that young people who are at present
eligible to vote could also become MPs.

Guardian

People who lived in glass houses should not throw
stones, warned Jones Major (Young Con) in the
adjournment debate last night. He was replying to
Opposition allegations that he was as thick as two
short planks. Mr Jones said that coming as it did from a
polytechnic rabble, the suggestion that he should run
home to his mummy was beneath contempt. It was
they, the Opposition, who should run home to their
mummies, or 'mums', as Mr Jones believed was the
more usual form of address in certain uncouth
quarters. He said that while sticks and stones might
break his bones, names would never hurt him.

The Commons were debating the motion, 'That in
the opinion of this House, the deserving poor deserve
all they get.'

Mr Cedric Faunterloy (Young Lib) said that he
believed it was Samuel Johnson who had said that a
woman's preaching was like a dog's walking on his
hinder legs: it was not done well, but it was suprising to
find it done at all. The same could be said about some
Hon Members who had spoken in the debate. Like the
death of Mark Twain, reports of their eloquence were
greatly exaggerated. Mr Faunterloy was reminded of a
story, probably apocryphal, about the late Sir Winston
Churchill and the late Clement Attlee. Told that Attlee
was modest, the great man had replied—

After Young Marxist and Young Trotskyist interrup-
tions, the Speaker cautioned the House against toilet-
roll throwing.

The House Monitor for Home Affairs, Mr Thomas
Brown, said that it was a jolly shame. Hon Members

had worked jolly hard to prepare for the debate and make it a success, some of them giving up togger practice in order to swot up quotations or print posters and handbills, and now a minority of cads and rotters were trying to wreck the whole evening. It was a jolly – (*interruption*).

Mr Speaker told the House that he was going to ask the Hon Member or Right Hon Member who had thrown a bread roll at the House Monitor for Home Affairs to see him privately behind the Speaker's chair after the debate. If no Hon Member or Right Hon Member came forward, then the Speaker had no alternative. The whole House would be kept in after Question Time tomorrow. (Cries of 'Oh!')

Mr Robert Cratchit (Young Soc) said that while the Speaker and others were spouting all this stuff from y'knew, Shakespeare and that, there were millions in the Third World who did not have enough to eat. Mr Cratchit asked the House to look at some of the y'knew, Hon Members opposite. They were so fat it was obscene. It was a totally undeniable fact that eighty per cent of the total wealth of this country was controlled by the totally unrepresentative five per cent who had been born with silver y'knew, spoons in their mouths, and this was totally unacceptable. Calling for a programme of Marxist determinism, the release of the Wormwood Scrubs Eight Hundred, an inquiry into police violence and y'knew, phone-tapping, a fair deal for the squatters of Hackney, a Parliamentary sit-in as a gesture of total solidarity with the escalating numbers of sociology lecturers being made redundant as a result of vicious and backward-looking cutbacks, and a total boycott of Japanese goods, Mr Cratchit went on to describe the Government as a tool of fascism. He was ruled out of order.

Miss Juliet Capulet (Young Pony League) said that she was very nervous. She just wanted to say that she agreed with what one of the previous speakers had said, that there was too much poverty. This applied not only to people but to animals. Miss Capulet was not ashamed to say that when she thought of what was happening to animals she sometimes cried, she really did. Miss Capulet did not know how the House could sit there, as it had done last night, debating the EEC common fisheries policy, when what was happening to animals was taking place. That was all Miss Capulet wanted to say.

Miss Violet E. Bott (Young Ratepayers) said that it just so happened that she had taken part in the fisheries debate so wittily castigated by the Hon Member, and while not having the Hon Member's wit, she would just like to ask exactly why the Hon Member thought that fish did not have feelings, or was this just a sample of her wit?

Mr T. Sawyer (Young Ind) said that fish did not have feelings.

Mr Wm. Brown (Young Empire Loyalists) said that fish did have feelings.

Mr Stalky Corkran (Young Nat Front) said that fish did not have feelings.

The Famous Five (Young Rock Pool Explorers' Alliance) said that fish did have feelings.

Mr Wm. Bunter (Young Con) said that fish did not have feelings.

Mr W. Brown said they they did, you knew.

Mr Bunter said that they did not, you knew.

Intervening, Mr D. Copperfield (Young Lib) asked the Hon Member how he knew that fish did not have feelings. Had he ever had a hook stuck in his mouth?

Mr Bunter said that he was not a fish. (Cries of, 'No, a whale more like!')

Mr Copperfield asked in that case, how did he know that fish did not have feelings? (Cries of, 'Answer! Answer!')

Mr Robert Cherry (Young Horseplay Assoc) said that there was only one way to settle the matter, by putting it to the vote.

The Speaker hoped that before forcing a division, the Hon Member would be guided by his experience as an older, he would not say wiser, Parliamentarian. Debate after debate and Bill after Bill were nowadays being brought to a standstill while the House voted on frivolous and irrelevant questions. The third reading of the Docks, Piers, Harbours, Canals and Inland Navigation Undertakings (Night Watchmen's Emoluments) Bill, for example, had been completely abandoned while the House divided on the issue of 'Who made God?' The democratic process was being brought into disrepute. If the House would be guided by him, he would ask the Whips to resume their places and call upon the Head Prefect to wind up what had on the whole been an informed and stimulating debate.

The Head Prefect and First Lord of the Treasury, Mr H. Flashman, said that while listening to Mr Speaker he had been reminded of some lines of he thought it was Victor Hugo: *'Souffrons, mais souffrons sur les cimes,'* or for the benefit of Hon Members opposite, 'If we must suffer, let us suffer nobly'. Mr Speaker had suffered the debate nobly. But was it not Philander Chase Johnson who had said, Cheer up, the worst was yet to come? The worst was yet to come. Mr Speaker would now have to nobly suffer, if he would forgive the split infinitive, the agony of hearing his praises sung by the Head Prefect. The Head Prefect believed it was John Wesley who had written, Do all the good you could, By all the means you could, In all the ways you could, In all the places you could, At all the times you could, To all the people you could, As long as ever you could. Those sentiments were embodied in Mr Speaker. The Head Prefect would ask the House to rise and give three resounding cheers. (*Cheers.*)

Miss Capulet said that if she could just have one more word, she had never meant to imply in her reference to the EEC Common Fisheries Policy that fish did not have feelings. She knew that they did, like all animals. She would crave the indulgence of the House to read a short statement about animals, particularly man's best friend the dog. It was in verse. When all your days were weary, and all the world seemed blue – (*Interruption.*)

Mr Speaker said that he advised the Hon Member who had just made that disgusting noise to own up at once or apply for the Chiltern Hundreds. The Speaker would count to ten. Some Hon Members must know who the culprit was. If they continued to shield him, the Serjeant-at-Arms would lock the doors and the House would sit all night if necessary until the offending Hon Member came forward. It was up to Hon Members. It did not matter to Mr Speaker. He had all the time in the world.

The House rose at 7.30 pm on the following Sunday.

Vulgar Boatmen

A Russian was bundled away by Soviet security men
after he began telling fishermen in a pub in Falmouth,
Cornwall, about life aboard his factory ship. The
incident happened when the seaman started
complaining to locals, with the aid of a phrase book, of
rats swarming round living quarters, women 'shared
out' by senior officers, and lack of time off on the
Daurra, which has been at sea for at least seven
months.

Guardian

Iss right how-d'you-do, serving in glorious Soviet merchant fleet (mused the night-watchman, packing his clay pipe with sawdust and striking a match against the capstan at the end of L——grad Wharf). Iss like book *Animal Farm* by Orwell, G. All downtrodden masses are equal but some are more downtrodden than others.

Take old tub Saucy S—— (the night-watchman

continued as he struck another match, the first one having failed to ignite). Me and my mates Ilya Ilyvitch and Ginger Gingenovitch signed on as sailormen to escape clutches of secret bobbies after getting into pub brawl in tap-room of Three Morose Lathe Operatives in year 19——. We set sail from this here wharf to pick up cargo of C—— from port of N——-upon-Tyne across N—— Sea. But afore we had lost sight of L——grad Reach we was all heartily wishing we was doing fifteen years down salt-mine in province of S——.

It was Ginger Gingenovitch what cracked first (went on the night-watchman, rummaging in his matchbox for another match with a head on it after the second one he had tried to light had snapped in two). Iss eating our dinner off herring-box in f'c'sle one day when Ginger Gingenovitch suddenly threw down his spoon and sez: 'Rat soup, rat soup! If I'm not sick o' rat soup! Iss rat soup day in, day out!'

At this Cookie draws himself up to his full 1.219 metres and sez, all sarky: 'Ho, excuse me, I was not aware we had Inspector from *Good Food Guide* on board. However, Comrade Ginger Gingenovitch, afore you casts any more aspersions at them what iss slaving away at hot wood-stove all morning, why don't you go and get second opinion from your mate Fay Maschlerevna, oo would tell you iss not rat soup what offends your Epicurean taste-buds, iss cat soup?'

Ilya Ilyvitch goes quite pale and sez in choked voice: 'Are you telling us, Cookie, that iss ship's cat, Tibbles Tibblesyvitch, we are eating?'

'Not all of it,' sez Cookie, 'I thought I would save head and boil it with nice pair o'boots for tomorrow's supper as bit o'change from fish-bone stew. Though Chairman of Praesidium alone knows why I bother, when Comrade Ginger Gingenovitch cannot tell difference between rat soup and cat soup. For your information we finished last of rats afore we left B—— Sea.'

'In that case,' I axed, fishing out of my soup small

174

furry creature what was as damp and dead as these flaming matches (continued the night-watchman), 'I would beg leave to inquire what this here is, assuming Tibbles Tibblesyvitch did not change sex and have kittens afore you murdered him.'

'In first place he was not murdered, he died o'pneumonia,' sez Cookie. 'In second place, iss not rat in your cat soup, Comrade Clever Dick Dickovitch, iss bat. It must have been in that soot what fell down ship's funnel into cooking-pot.'

Ginger Gingenovitch pushed aside his soup bowl, what was at once grabbed by one of crew oo was licking dried porridge off of floor, as it was not his turn to have any dinner. 'Iss last straw,' sez Ginger. 'Oo'll volunteer to go and put our case to Skipper?'

After full, free and democratic discussion, crew voted that Ginger Gingenovitch should complain to Skipper about our conditions as it was his idea, and that as we was his mates, Ilya Ilyvitch and me should go with him, to stop him accidentally falling overboard. So after a bit o'prodding with coal shovels and pick-handles to reassure us that rest of lads was behind us, Ginger, Ilya and me set off for Skipper's cabin on —— Deck.

We couldn't agree which one of us was to have honour of knocking on Skipper's door. I thought it should be Ginger, Ginger thought it should be me as he didn't want to take all limelight, and Ilya said he didn't mind who got credit so long as it wasn't him. We was seeing if we had kopek between us so's we could toss for it when we heard voices coming from inside Skipper's cabin.

Fust we heard Chief Purser's voice axing: 'Wot do you feel like for dinner, Skipper Skippenovitch? 'Ow about champagne and oysters as a change from claret and smoked salmon?' Then we hears Skipper. 'We can't have oysters when there's no P in the month, you ignorant pillock,' he sez. 'Besides, I wants some more o'

175

that there caviar, follered by steak and chips, follered by fresh strawberries and cream, follered by nice Uzbekistan Rarebit. But fust off, you can open another magnum and hand round them cigars.'

Arter that there's popping of corks and clinking of glasses, then we hears slaps and giggles and another voice sez: 'Oo, he's got hands like octopus. Is cheeky boy.' Then yet another voice sez: 'Iss right saucebox.'

Ginger Gingenovitch nudges me in ribs and whispers, all excited like: 'Dirty old ram's got women in there!' But just as we all three started scuffling to peep through keyhole, door was thrown open and we fell into cabin at feet of Chief Purser. Skipper was lying on sofa having grapes dropped into his mouth by comrade woman well-known in L——grad as comrade woman of streets. Another comrade woman well-known in L—— grad as Madame Whiplash Karenina was chasing First Mate round chart-table, while third comrade woman, well-known in L——grad as comrade man, was dancing with Second Mate.

'What is meaning of this intrusion?' roars Skipper. 'Why aren't you lily-livered comrades freezing on deck or swabbing cockroach-infested latrines? And stand to attention when your captain is ranting and raving at you!'

Arter a lot more o'that sort o'thing he demanded agin to know what we wanted. Ginger wouldn't open his mouth and Ilya couldn't open his mouth, and it was only hunger pangs at sight of all them grapes and big bowls of caviar what made me open mine.

'Please, comrade, sir,' I stammers. 'Iss deputation, to axe if you could spare us crust o' bread. Your crew ain't had nothing to eat except ship's cat for three days, and some of lads iss growing restless.'

'What's this? Mutiny?' Skipper shouts, foaming at mouth. 'What ship do you think you're on – bloody Potemkin? Any more o' that kind o'talk and I'll have you in ship's hospital psychiatry wing so fast your feet won't touch bloody deck!'

'Iss pity in some ways we're not living in reactionary reign of despicable Tsar,' sez Madame Whiplash Karenina. 'You could have given them knout.'

'They'd only have etten it,' Skipper growls. Then blowing cigar-smoke in our faces he sez: 'Get back to your quarters, you festering comrades. Iss giving masked ball for officers and few friends this evening and I don't want it spoiled by seeing scum like you licking your scurvy lips while we're tucking into chocolate liqueurs and ice-cream shaped like swan.'

Tails between legs, we slunk back to f'c'sle, only to find that Cookie had chopped up our bunks to feed wood-stove so he could keep cat soup lukewarm for middle watch. That did it for me, Ginger and Ilya. As soon as we docked at N——-upon-Tyne we jumped ship.

O' course (concluded the night-watchman, hurtling his box of matches into the sea, then throwing his sawdust-packed clay-pipe to the ground and dancing up and down on it), we was picked up at once by KGB and returned to L——grad chained up in coal-hold. But travelling as cargo was like going fust-class on QE—after what we'd been used to.

University Challenge

I went up to the University of Life at the unusually late age of fifteen, on a scholarship grant from the School of Hard Knocks. I read history, sociology, biology, Eng. Lit., economics, politics, wrestling and law. I became President of the Union and a member of the co-operative which edited our wall newspaper. I was sent down for smoking a pipe on Founder's Patch, a cinderpaved quadrangle behind the Co-op Butcher's, where the 'bloods' or 'swells' had decreed that only Woodbines could be smoked.

Returning to the sprawling campus after an interval of thirty years, I find much change. The biology pavilion in the University Park, where we used to experiment on a girl called Mavis Parkin, has been burned down. The Union Building, which I recall doubled as a corporation bus shelter, has had all its windows smashed in and is now boarded up. There are new halls of residence but they have a neglected air: the lifts don't work and there is a smell of urine on the communal landings.

Today's graduates seem a dispirited lot, much given to hanging about outside their rooms complaining that there is nothing to effing do. On the other hand, the wall newspaper still flourishes; it now extends over the entire campus and, thanks to exciting new technological developments, is now printed in durable aerosol rather than chalk. The editorial policy is that United rules, and that this is OK.

Eheu fugaces! Many old faces are gone. Ma Hopkins, Old Moore Reader in Palmistry and Tea-leaves, now lies under the sod. Likewise Police Constable Booth, sometime Lecturer on Law and Applied Violence. My language tutor, Spotty Bullock, is taking a prolonged sabbatical at I believe, Pentonville. And Mr Tooley, who in my day graced the Weavers' Arms Chair in Modern History, is in the geriatric ward.

Dear old Tooley! He had two lectures I recall – one on Influence on the Battle of the Somme by the First Battalion, the King's Own Yorkshire Light Infantry, and one on Churchill's Role in the General Strike. Speaking entirely without notes, he could captivate an audience simply by clutching that audience's sleeve. Some of his characteristic phrases – such as, 'We was up to our bollocks in mud, mate,' and 'You tell me what that bugger has ever done for the working man,' became famous. I have often thought that A. J. P.

178

Taylor owes a tremendous debt to Mr Tooley.

The City of Dreaming Cooling-Towers is barely recognizable to a middle-aged alumnus but the Weavers' Arms still stands and the Modern History Chair is now occupied by a young man named Gomersall. Because he is the son of fatty Gomersall, whose rooms adjoined mine when I was a freshman and whose Ph.D. thesis, 'Some Errors in the W. D. & H. O. Wills Cigarette Card Series, "Famous British Footballers"', created a major controversy leading to the resignation of Ginger Cuthbertson as Visiting Reader in Football Facts, I made it my business to attend one of his lectures.

It was poor stuff in my view. Young Gomersall chose as his theme the political career of Mr Enoch Powell, with special reference to rivers of blood. With so many students from the former colonies now enrolled at the University of Life, here was material for a splendid academic fireworks display. Yet it made no impact at all. Gomersall, I believe, made two errors. First, his research was indifferent – he was surely on questionble ground in asserting that it was bleeding Powell what fetched the bleeding darkies over here in the first bleeding place. Second, he should not have tried to compete with the topless go-go dancer who is now an integral part of the Weavers' Arms curriculum.

Leaving modern history behind me I ventured further into the past: to the corner of Sebastopol Street where Spotty Bullock used to hold his famous seminars; to the subterranean public convenience (now, alas, bricked up) beneath whose glass-tiled canopy, so reminiscent of the Radcliffe Camera, many a provoking essay was penned; to Founder's Patch where the proctors once discovered a third-year biology student having it off rotten with Mavis Parkin in broad daylight (he was rusticated as far as the Welsh Dairy where he made his escape in a bread-van); and so to my old rooms, now occupied by a freckle-faced youth reading Skateboard Maintenance. The engineering side, which had little to offer except a short course in Bicycle Puncture Studies when I was up, is very strong these days.

The youth's mother, mistaking me for a social worker, invited me in to inspect the rising damp which she said the faculty would do nothing about although she had complained times without number. The rooms where I long ago burned so much midnight oil – at one time actually setting them on fire when trying to study *Fifty Great Tragedies of Land, Sea and Air* (required syllabus reading) under the bedclothes by candlelight – were very much transformed.

Gone were the cheap leatherette-covered armchairs and the old horsehair sofa: in their place a three-piece suite in off-white simulated hide with lozenges of lime-green. Gone was the shabby old table with its tasselled plush cloth, where I pored over back numbers of the *Daily Worker* before the Political Science finals; now there was a proper dining table of some highly-polished wood like sucked toffee, with sideboard and chairs to match. A fitted carpet with a lively design of clefs and piano-keys had replaced the worn linoleum. The old wireless set, of course, had given way to a 26-inch television screen on which was reflected such an exact replica of the room I had just entered that I took it, momentarily, for a mirror: then I realized I was watching *Crossroads*.

Truly, in material terms, my alma mater has gone up in the world. If the University of Life is not yet Ivy League, it is near the top of the Privet Union.

I asked my young skateboarding friend about social activities. The Debating Society, which used to meet in the University quarry to discuss such questions as whether it was possible for a girl to get pregnant if she did it standing up – did that still thrive?

Nah. Nothing to effing talk about, was there?

The Film Society, then, that made a cult-figure of Betty Grable at its Saturday night meetings in the

Regal Cinema?

Nah. It was all effing bingo these days, wasn't it?

The ULPLRC? (University of Life Park Lake Rowing Club, where I earned my blue.) Nah. The Dining Club, that assembled weekly at Sam's Café? Nah. The Literary Institute, where budding Leavises cut their critical milk-teeth on *Health and Efficiency*? Nah.

What, then, did present-day students do with their time? Nothing much. Watch telly and that. Smash a few windows and that. Chase a few nig-nogs and that. Get pissed and that. Nothing else to do, was there, in this rotten hole?

This lacklustre spirit, I am afraid, is reflected in academic standards. For example, a banner headline in the current edition of the wall newspaper reads: SANDRA PAWSON SCREW'S. No sub-editor would have let through that superfluous apostrophe in my day; nor would we have tolerated the sloppy colloquial substitute for an Anglo-Saxon verb.

Despondently, I continued my journey across the campus. I paused on the asphalt forecourt of Hugh Dalton House, one of the new halls of residence, to watch a sparsely-attended class on the Dynamics of Milk-bottle Throwing – a new subject to me. Some first-year men had decided on a rag and were stuffing one of their number in a rubbish-chute, which they then set on fire. A Freshman was urinating from an eighth-floor balcony. A Senior Lecturer in Law and Order, wearing traditional academic robes – mackintosh belted with string and cloth cap – shouted across to the Hugh Dalton Reader in Home Economics – equally resplendent in curlers and pinafore – that they were destructive bastards and ought to be locked up. As he later reported to the Pro-vice Chancellors in the Weavers' Arms, they came back at him with a right mouthful.

Where, I asked myself, has the University of Life gone wrong? How has it lost its thrust, its zest, its flavour? Why does it no longer turn out distinguished graduates when it is easier than ever to win a foundation scholarship to one of the more orthodox establishments such as Essex? Why, for example, has the University of Life not produced a single new novelist in the last fifteen years? Where are its poets? Its painters? Its promising politicians?

It may be true, as the Regius Professor of Local Government asserted to me, that the Government is deliberately starving the University of grant-aid for vitally-needed community centres and other vitally-needed amenities, with the deliberate object of deliberately creating and maintaining a two-nation economy. On the other hand, in my day there was no grant-aid to be starved of; the entire campus was our community centre and we would not have recognized an amenity if it had walked up and bitten us on the leg.

It may also be true that following its expansion programme in the 'sixties the University of Life is now architecturally a disaster area. You can no longer tell one college from another and many of the University's departments and student hostels are now 'in the middle of nowhere', as one undergraduate after another put it, instead of being an integral part of city life. This has created a town *v* gown atmosphere which leads to football hooliganism and all the rest of it. But again on the other hand, we grey-haired alumni had our share of drabness and social deprivation, and it made us all the more determined to get as much as we possibly could out of the University curriculum.

The key to the mystery is probably in the slight change of wording in the University of Life motto. In my day it was 'Don't let the bastards get you down'. Now, so I gather, it is 'The bastards have got us down'.

Is There a PR Man in the House?

MPs are being accused of forwarding their business
interests in the Commons.

News item

MR STRING asked the Minister of State for Odds and
Sods whether he had lost his cigarette lighter.

THE MINISTER OF STATE FOR ODDS AND SODS (Mr
Albert Watchstrap): No, sir.

MR STRING: Is the Minister aware that if he *had* lost
his cigarette lighter, he could find no better replacement
than the Ee-zee-flame disposable gas lighter, available
in a wide variety of colours or in simulated crocodile
skin, at all leading tobacconists? Is he further aware
that I have two gross of the things in my locker, and
that I am in a position to let him have any quantity he
likes at cost, or could slip him half a dozen in return for
free mention of the Maltimilk Bedtime Drink, a
nourishing and sustaining beverage in which I have not
the smallest interest?

MR WATCHSTRAP: My Hon Friend's concern for the
Maltimilk Bedtime Drink does him credit, and I will try
to work in a reference to its nutritive qualities in
tomorrow's debate on the sprat and mackerel fishing
limits. I may even sing a short jingle, if Mr Speaker will
permit it. However, I cannot reiterate too strongly that
I am all right for cigarette lighters. I would draw the
Hon Gentleman's attention to my reply to the Hon
Member for Sludgeborough (Mr George – You Want
The Best Seats I Have Them – Breadstick) on 25
October last, when I drew attention to the urgent need
for two front stalls at the Splendide Theatre, any night
except Monday.

MRS PANSCRUB asked the Minister of State for Odds
and Sods what he was doing tonight.

MR WATCHSTRAP: If it is any of the Hon Lady's
business, I am going to a reception to launch a new
Magi-Kamera which, retailing at a recommended price
of £48, will take pictures under water. Fun for all the

family. From all High Street chemists, or fill in the handy coupon in today's *Hansard*.

MRS PANSCRUB: I only ask because I could guarantee the Minister a better class of vol-au-vent, with all the Champagne he can drink thrown in, were he to accompany me to the Invitation only Celebrity Birthday Party for the Soho Sauna Clinic and Massage Parlour. 24A Bottle Street, W. Twelve, yes twelve, gorgeous hostesses.

MR SPEAKER: That is not a question.

MRS PANSCRUB: Perhaps you were not aware, Mr Speaker, that I was accompanying my invitation with a raising of the right eyebrow, a slight cocking of the head and a suggestive 'come hither' motion of the left shoulder. I submit, on a Point of Order, that these gesticulations could be taken to indicate that my words were of an interrogative nature.

MR SPEAKER: I don't care what you were doing, you are out of order. And since the proceedings of this House have been interrupted, I might as well inform

184

the Hon Member for Clogthorpe East that if those are mail order catalogues he is distributing along the Front Bench, he too is out of order. Let us get on.

MR CARDBOARD: asked the Minister of State for Odds and Sods how he was off for golf balls.

MR WATCHSTRAP: I have nothing to add to the Written Answer I gave my Hon Friend on the third of this month, when I intimated that I could do with some.

MR CARDBOARD: Is the Minister aware that a year's supply will be his, with a new set of clubs thrown in, on the day he introduces into debate – I care not which debate – the phrase or saying 'Naval Blend, the mild cigarette with the low-tar content'?

MR WATCHSTRAP: That might be difficult, but I will bear my Hon Friend's suggestion in mind.

MR TROUSERS asked the Minister of State for Bits and Pieces what steps he is taking to ensure that his family does not get that run-down feeling during the winter months.

THE MINISTER OF STATE FOR BITS AND PIECES (Mr Doorknob): I see that they drink Maltimilk Bedtime Drink every night.

MR TROUSERS: While appreciating the Hon Gentleman's good intentions may I point out that he has given this House a most unsatisfactory answer, and that his family would be free from colds and chilblains by taking Blenkinsop's Blackcurrant Lozenges regularly?

MR DOORKNOB: I have never heard of the lozenges the Hon Gentleman mentions.

Mr Briefcase rose —

MR SPEAKER: Order. The Hon Member for Scumville North is parading up and down this chamber sporting a sandwich-board which bears the legend, 'Blenkinsop's Blackcurrant Lozenges, They Keep Your Kiddies On Their Toes'. I cannot have that.

MR BRIEFCASE: I was merely trying to draw the Minister's attention to—

HON MEMBERS: Sit down!

MR BRIEFCASE: That is easier said than done.

MR STRING.   asked the Minister of State for Bits and Pieces whether he had lost his cigarette lighter.

MR SPEAKER: Order. I cannot have that either. The Hon Member for Filthbury has already asked that Question, of another Minister.

MR STRING: If you will bear with me, Mr Speaker, this is a separate question for which I have booked prime time by paying the appropriate sum. However,in deference to your ruling, I will phrase it differently. With what does the Minister light his cigarettes?

MR DOORKNOB: If the Hon Gentleman has in mind my daily supply of Naval Blend, the mild cigarette with the low-tar content, the answer is matches.

MR WATCHSTRAP: On a point of order, Mr Speaker, that is my line.

MR CARDBOARD: On a point of order, the offer of a year's supply of golf balls with set of clubs thrown in, no questions asked, was quite specifically offered to the first Minister to mention Naval Blend, the mild cigarette with the low-tar content. Runners-up to get one bot sparkling wine, embossed score-pad and one doz plastic tees, as laid down in *Dodd's Parliamentary Companion*.

MR WATCHSTRAP: Very well, I would only beg the Hon Gentleman not to come running to me when next he wants to advertise holiday flatlets in Spain. This is a Government Department we're trying to run here, not *Dalton's* bleeding *Weekly*.

MR SPEAKER: Order. I shall rule on this later. The Hon Member for Filthbury has a supplementary.

MR STRING: I was only going to ask the Minister if, seeing that he uses matches to light his Naval Blend, the mild cigarette with the low-tar content, he has ever thought about the Ee-zee-flame disposable gas lighter?

MR DOORKNOB: (singing) Ee-zee-flame, Ee-zee-flame, Snap it on, Snap it off, Make Light of Everything with Eeeeee-zeeeee-flame!

186

HON MEMBERS: It's dee-*light*-ful!

MR ASHTRAY: And is the Minister aware that he can now buy an Ee-zee-flame refillable model at all leading stores? That supplies of the same are available at the Discount Cash-and-Carry in Another Place? And that if he has any difficulty in obtaining his Ee-zee flame refillable lighter, he has only to apply to the Chief Whip for list of stockists?

MR DOORKNOB: I am obliged to my Hon Friend for that information.

MR TROUSERS asked the Minister of State for This and That what precaution he is taking about guarding his children from coughs and chills.

MR SPEAKER: If that is another plug for Blenkinsop's Blackcurrant Lozenges, it is out of order. Use more soap. Drink more tea. Book now for *Aladdin* at the Theatre Royal, Bowelthorpe. Pendlebury's Pork Sausages are sizzling good. Who goes home?

MR STRING: I do, Mr Speaker, in a Speedwell Door-to-Door mini-cab, phone this number night or day, our 24-hour-service will get you to your home at competitive rates.

A Drunk's Christmas in Soho

Years and beers and cheers ago, when I was a boyo, when there was more slag in Old Compton Street than in the valleys, when we swallowed and wallowed all day and night in caverns that smelt like armpits, and nuzzled and nestled in armpits like taverns, I don't mean taverns, the word I just said, caverns; back in those sprawling, crawling, falling, your-glasses-please-gentlemen-calling times, it snowed and it snowed.

But here a brass-blonde nursing a gin-and-It like a new born babe says: 'It snowed last year too, dear. I fell

on my bum outside the French pub and you kissed it better.'

'But that was not the same snow,' I say. 'Our snow came shawling down and swam and drifted over the bat-black, hat-black, cat-black, mat-black, sat-black, rat-black, fat-black ha ha ha ha ha excuse me ahem.'

'Get on with it, then.'

'Listen, tight lady of the light. As you were: night. Listen to what I am telling you. Listen, because this is very interesting. Listen, because this is the most interesting, winteresting, splinteresting, pinteresting—'

'Oh God, he's off again.'

'One Christmas was so much like another, in those lost boy years spewed up in sawdust and gone out of sight except for the little animals I sometimes see a moment before sleep, that I can never remember whether I was pissed for six days and six nights when I was twenty-five or for twenty-five days and nights when I was who's got my drink?'

'You've got to humour him, you know. Were there drinks then, too?'

'Rivers and oceans of them. I rode in a barrel down a Niagara of rum, then bobbed in a dimpled bottle across the seven C's. Calavados, Crême de menthe, cherry brandy, Charrington's Export and look, I'm not a complete bloody fool, you know, this is ginger ale.'

'It's Scotch and ginger, dear. Was there singing?'

'Such singing as a child cradled in sleep hears when the lark-choir caged in dreams cries at the dew-drop morning. HO! THIS IS NUMBER ONE, AND THE FUN HAS JUST BEGUN, ROLL ME OVER, LAY ME DOWN AND DO IT AGAIN . . .'

'Come along, dear, the landlord has very kindly invited us to leave. Mind the steps.'

'WE THREE KINGS OF ORIENT ARE, ONE IN A TAXI, ONE IN A CAR . . . Where are we now?'

'In a club, dear. The one you're not barred from. Tell us about the jokes.'

'But I haven't told you about the singing yet. Such singing as a child cradled in sleep—'

'You did mention the singing, dear. You told that policeman in Leicester Square all about the singing, and I said I'd look after you. Tell us about the jokes.'

'In those Christmases gone-by, when the snow-thatched roofs glistened like icing-sugar in the dew-drop morning, and the lark-choir caged in dreams cried at the children cradled in sleep, there was this thick-mick, bog-fog Irishman who was trying to change this electric light bulb—'

'Keep your voice down, dear, the barman comes from Belfast. And I'm sure you won't mind, but you've just bought my friend a bottle of Champagne. I've put the rest of your money in your top pocket.'

'In those chestnut-pulling Christmases gone by, not

189

chestnut-pulling, cracker-pulling, in those chestnut-cracking, cracker-pulling, pulling-cracking, stocking-filling, pillowcase-stuffing, turkey-plucking, stop-me-if-you've-heard-it Christmases gone by, such jokes were told as would set double chins bouncing like jellies and bosoms heaving like chapel-picnic blancmanges, and nipples the size and substance of glacé cherries would balloon from their sequined moorings and—'

'Were there barmaids, in those days?'

'Of course there were barmaids, you stupid ignorant cow! Whose nipples the size and substance of glacé cherries do you think would balloon from their sequined moorings, if not the double-chin bouncing, bosom-heaving barmaids? And I'll tell you another thing about those triple-Scotch, nipple-touch, tipple-much Christmases gone by, they didn't water the sodding whisky.'

'Come on, dear.'

'Where going now?'

'Back to my place.'

'And when it was rat-back night and the frolicking and rollicking were over, and drunks lay like skittles in the alleys and policemen with fat lips frog-marched poets up the snow sleet, Bow-street steps, and the yule frog correction yule log hissed and sighed then crackled into powder like the snow thatched roofs crumbling like icing-sugar in the dew-drop morning and the lark-choir, no stuff the lark-choir, you've made me lose my bloody thread now.'

'Sorry, dear, I was just taking a pound note for the taxi fare. I've put the rest of your money in your back pocket.'

'Back-pocket Venuses, slim as Venus pencils, flitted out of that cat-pack night and scrawled and scribbled their indelible kisses over the fat-lipped poet's frog-slobbering cheeks, then with calligraphic fingers scratched copperplate pothooks across his parchment belly, oh Christ.'

'What's the matter, dear?'

'I'm going to be sick. A Vesuvius of light ale, rum and peppermint, Scotch on the rocks, gin and tonic, and that green stuff we were drinking on the alley-cat-scuttling bomb site, churns and heaves and then erupts, rumbling to the surface like a Rhondda pit-cage and spewing through frog-slobbering lips with the whirling, swirling force of a clogged-up fountain in a vomatorium. Why is there always tomato in it?'

'Out you get, dear.'

'Where going this time?'

'The taxi-driver has very nicely asked us to walk the rest of the way, dear. Its just round the corner.'

'And peeping round the corner of all the years, as a child peeps through church-steeple fingers at the tangerine-smelling tin-toy-promising stocking on the patchwork quilted horizon, I see a young man in his prime staggering through the Notting Hill, Rotting Hill tag-end-and-bobtail of Christmas and bawling at the Yule-frog dawn, 'TWAS ON THE GOOD SHIP VENUS, YOU REALLY SHOULD HAVE SEEN US—'

'Come to the Presents, dear.'

'There were Presents for everyone. There were Turkeys, plucked from the Food Hall at Harrods, and pressed on the doorman at Claridge's as a tip for not letting us in. There were shiny half-crowns for news-vendors, and sweet quires of the *Evening Standard* for the foot-stamping, No 11-damn-and-blasting-bus queues. There were crisp-and-even fivers for the commission-aires of night clubs, and teddy-bears that mooed for the cow-face hostesses. And in the senseless, Wenceslas-singing evening, all the barmaids, with nipples the size and substance of glacé cherries, would smirk and say "You shouldn't have" as they dabbed bedroom-smelling scent on their bouncing, heaving—'

'You've told me about the barmaids already, dear. Get back to the Presents.'

'In a minute. I'm going to be sick again. A Vesuvius of—'

'Just lean against the lamp-post, dear. And get back

to the Presents, to take your mind off what you've had to drink. Were there Presents for your lady-friends?'

'Oh, yes. The street-girls were paved with gold, those Christmases of so long ago.'

'That's the idea, dear, I've left you enough for your bus fare. It's in your side pocket. I'd ask you in, but my landlady doesn't like it. Merry Christmas, dear,' says the brass-blonde who nursed her gin-and-It all night like a new-born babe.

'Merry Christmas,' I say, and then I lay me down to sleep.

Blackboard Jungle Warfare

The discussion in the launderette, where a cross-section of launderette-users gather each week to wash their smalls, has turned to the question of school uniforms. It was the silly season and it was the common view that barring rape and inflation there was little else to talk about.

'I was shocked when our only daughter Gillian, 14, was sent home from school for wearing a T-shirt advertising a well-known brand of contraceptive,' said Mrs Biginshaw as she separated her coloureds from a pile of washing. 'Gillian, 36–24–37 is big for her age, and gym-slips are costly. We will not give way, it is the principle. We are keeping Gillian at home and in the meantime we are writing to our MP.'

'Same as our Marlene, 13,' said Mrs Mulcromby. 'She came home in tears, banned from sitting her O-levels because teachers claimed her leatherette hot pants were too revealing.'

'CHEEKY!' chorused the regulars.

'I remember that,' said Mrs Corrigan. 'Marlene's Oh! Levels upset teachers.'

'Bottom of the class, she'd be,' said Mrs Biginshaw, 'But curvaceous Gillian was not showing anything she shouldn't. She is being persecuted.'

'So is buxom Marlene,' continued Mrs Mulcromby. 'We thought it sensible for her to wear comfortable clothes to sit her exams. It was a hot day – I remember passing the remark to my husband, progress chaser Alfred Mulcromby: Phew! What a scorcher, I said, Yes, he said, eighty degrees, he said. It's flaming June, he said. An all-wool uniform would have been bad for her concentration. Also, delicate Marlene has been ill and we had a note from her doctor allowing her to wear the offending garment. We are getting up a petition to the Queen.'

'As a teacher in a large London comprehensive school – not the one from which the girls have been banned – I could not agree less with parents who keep their children at home after disagreements about school uniform,' said Miss Latimer, feeding tights into the spin-drier. 'Rules are meant to be kept. Not all mothers are sensible, I recall one case where a boy reported for lessons dressed as a Red Indian.'

'Yaroo! Crikey, you rotters!' said Mrs Biginshaw. 'But Gillian, a runner-up in a local beauty contest this year, was not infringing shool rules. Other girls wear T-shirts without comment. She is being picked on because of an incident earlier this term.'

'Was that when rebel Gillian refused to eat school dinners?' asked Mrs Corrigan.

'That's right. It sparked off a protest by parents against what they claimed were too stodgy meals. Housewives, many of them pushing prams demonstrated at the school gates.'

'I know,' said Mrs Ridgeway. 'Policemen, some of them with walkie-talkies, were called in to control the crowds. School staff blamed Gillian for the outcry.'

'Now every morning stay-at-home Gillian studies from library books at the kitchen table of our three-bedroom £4.50-a-week council house,' said Mrs Bigin-shaw. 'Soon she will start work in the office of a firm of brick merchants.'

'Hot pants Marlene had lost three pounds through the worry of being barred from taking her exams,' said Mrs Mulcromby. 'She needed three O-levels to qualify for the job of messenger girl with an oil company. Tory group councillors are said to be taking up her case any day now.'

'You want to get her on *Nationwide*,' said Mrs Corrigan. 'There'd be sure to be questions in the House after this kind of a hot pants TV storm.'

Mr Gray, an occasional visitor to the launderette who was washing some Wincyette blankets, spoke next. 'Both these cases have been blown up out of all proportion,' he said. 'As you ladies know, I am a spokesman for the Education Committee and I have seen the relevant files. A thirteen-year-old girl was suspended from classes because her dress was con-sidered unsuitable. At the same school, another girl was sent home because her shorts were distracting other pupils who were sitting O-levels. It is not true that the second girl's teacher called her "Big-bum". It is not true that he pinched her and that she slapped his face, although there was a scuffle when the girl was ordered from the premises. The incident is being investigated and a report has been called for. We have every confidence in the teaching staff. May I borrow a tablespoon of your soap crystals, Mrs Ridgeway? Beyond that, I do not wish to comment.'

'Sounds more like a blackboard jungle to me,' said Mrs Ridgeway.

'I can tell you one thing,' said Mrs Mulcromby. 'We are demanding action against the teacher who pinched Marlene's bottom. A doctor who examined her said there were bruises on the lower part of her body.'

'First I've heard about teacher in pinching row,' said Mrs Corrigan.

'Police advised us not to discuss the matter,' explained Mrs Mulcromby.

'They want to hush it up,' said Mrs Biginshaw. 'As far as raven-haired Gillian is concerned, we will not be silenced. A letter has been sent to the Education authorities.'

'As far as I am aware, no communication has been received,' said Mr Gray.

A quiet man rinsing socks in the corner, known to the regulars only as a consultant psychiatrist with a practice in Harley Street, interjected: 'Although I do not know the facts in these particular cases, other than what I have heard in the launderette, such incidents are common, particularly in the summer months. In my view, teaching staff are largely to blame.'

'Teachers caned, ' said Mrs Corrigan.

'Exactly. They do not realize that children are growing up quicker than ever, and that more and more mothers are ringing up the *News of the World* every time a healthy, photogenic adolescent is sent home from school.'

'I didn't ring up the *News of the World*,' said Mrs Biginshaw, 'I leave all that side to my agent.'

'So do I,' agreed Mrs Mulcromby. 'He got me on "World at One" last week. I spoke for mothers everywhere. We are fed up to the back teeth of being pushed around by what I called petty tyrants and pocket dictators.'

'Anyway, I can't stand about gossiping all day,' said Mrs Biginshaw, gathering up her washing. 'I've got to cook dinner for my husband Geoffrey, forty-eight, an unemployed zipper machinist, and after that I must send a telegram to the Education Secretary, demanding intervention.'

'Same time next week, everybody?' asked Mrs Corrigan.

'That's right, dear. We'll have a little chat about the chemist who caused a furore in a town's shopping

195

centre by branding local housewives as "shoplifters, pick-up girls and amateur prostitutes".'

Popish Plot

Clogthorpe District Council's Parks, Recreation Grounds and Leisure committee, under the chairmanship of Cllr Enoch Bulge, yesterday considered the question of inviting His Holiness the Pope to favour the borough with a state visit, official visit, walkabout, call it what you would, should his no doubt crowded itinerary in the United Kingdom permit it.

Introducing the motion, Cllr Bulge said the Pope needed no introduction. Although new to the job, he had endeared himself to countless millions. He had an easy manner and would fit in easily. Also, there was the prestige to be considered. The *Clogthorpe Mercury's* Religious Affairs Correspondent, Mr Booth, had been unable to dig up any reference to any Pope ever setting foot in the British Isles, let alone the borough of Clogthorpe. Even if the Pontiff could only make it for lunch and not stay overnight at the Clogthorpe Holiday Inn, it would be an undoubted feather in the local authority's cap.

Cllr Parkin said that according to the motion on the agenda in front of him, the proposal was to invite the No 1 man, that was to say, the Pope himself. There was absolutely no suggestion of asking him to send in a substitute, which in Cllr Parkin's humble opinion would be a defeatist way of going about it.

Cllr Bulge asked Cllr Parkin what he was talking about.

Cllr Parkin replied that they had started out by discussing an official visit by the Pope, and they were finishing up debating a brief lunchtime stopover by this Pontiff chap.

Cllr Bulge said they were one and the same person.

Apologizing for wasting the committee's time, Cllr Parkin said that he was a methodist and not up in these matters. Talk about mumbo-jumbo, these Catholics were worse than the Freemasons.

Cllr Nepworth asked what was wrong with the Freemasons.

Cllr Hopcraft said that he was sure Cllr Parkin had meant no offence, and if Cllr Nepworth found it beneficial to his business interests to roll up his trouser leg and play silly beggars, it was a free country. As to the motion before committee, Clogthorpe was a borough of plain folk, in fact they were renowned for their plainness, and if this Pope was going to be carried around the Ernest Bevin Trading Estate on that throne thing as seen on telly, all Cllr Hopcraft could say was that it would make a change from the annual Sunday Schools procession and he hoped and trusted his colleagues liked the smell of incense.

Cllr Tweedyman thought that Cllr Hopcraft had put his finger on the fly in the ointment or gentleman of African extraction in the woodpile. There were few Catholics in Clogthorpe. There might be a few Irish up in the Clement Attlee Overspill Conurbation, but that was about it. If the Pope did come to Clogthorpe, how would anyone know whether to stand up, kneel down, raise their hats or how's your father? Were the womenfolk supposed to wear veils, or what? It was a question of your protocol. Cllr Tweedyman didn't want His Holiness to leave Clogthorpe thinking 'What a lot of ignorant burks'.

Cllr Bulge said the point was well taken. He was sure the Vatican in its wisdom would be able to provide a Xeroxed sheet of guidelines, the same as what Buckingham Palace had promised to come up with in the event of his Royal Highness Prince Charles ever taking up the council's standing invitation to become honorary life president of the Chamber of Commerce Hang-Gliding Association.

Cllr Sludgeworth said that he would like to get down to the nitty-gritty and consider the problem of feeding His Holiness's face. He hoped that the council would for once be able to rise above the level of the usual Official Meat Tea. Although still given the cold shoulder by Mr Egon so-called Ronay, Clogthorpe's culinary establishments were moving with the times and there was now a perfectly acceptable Italian restaurant, namely the Sorrento Pizzeria, in the Poulson Shopping Mall. The Management had very kindly offered to do a sit-down meal at cost, provided spaghetti hoops was acceptable as a main dish and the Pope posed for souvenir photographs.

On a point of information, Cllr Bulge said that the Pope was not in fact an Eyetie.

Cllr Ackerman said that the chairman was well-informed, he would give him that. For himself, Cllr Ackerman did not care whether the Pope was Italian, Welsh, Pakistani, or Chinese, it was the principle of the thing. The council would be creating a precedent. Give one religious leader the run of the Civic Centre and where would it all end? They would have scientologists descending on the borough by the coachload. They would have that Ayatollah or whatever he called himself squatting on the steps of the old Corn Exchange. Why not invite the new leader of China, Mr What was his bloody name now, Dung it always sounded like to Cllr Ackerman, and have done?

Supporting Cllr Ackerman, Cllr Potter asked what the Pope had ever done for Clogthorpe.

Cllr Nepworth said that was just the kind of narrow, stupid, shortsighted, bigoted, pigheaded, moronic remark he had come to expect of Cllr Potter. He would remind all present that it was just such an attitude that had coloured the council's deliberations when he (Cllr

Nepworth) had proposed offering the Freedom of Clogthorpe to Mr Jasper Carrott, long before he had become a household name. What had been the result? The result had been that while the council had hemmed and hawed, Mr Carrott had gone on to have his own TV show, thus putting himself in the Birmingham-Manchester-Leeds bracket as regards civic honours, and the opportunity for the borough to attach itself to the coat-tails of his reputation was now gone forever.

Cllr Potter said that while sticks and stones might break his (Cllr Potter's) back, names would never hurt him, especially when emanating from a certain source. He did think, however, that some councillors should declare their own interests in these matters before launching on their usual tirade of mindless abuse. In the case of the Jasper Carrott invite, it was surely common ground that a certain councillor's daughter was the presenter of the Radio Clogthorpe chat-show, 'Clogthorpe at One', and that getting Jasper Carrott on the programme would have done no harm at all to her promotion prospects. Turning to the question of His Holiness the Pope, Cllr Potter would only ask, through the chair, which councillor was managing director of Nepworth's Novelty Warehouse (Trade Only), and whether it was or was not a fact that said gentleman had just taken delivery of three gross of nun dolls which crossed themselves when you pulled a cord?

Cllr Sludgeworth, saying that it was coming to something when one public servant made such grave accusations against another, asked the chairman for a ruling on whether Cllr Nepworth should have declared such an interest.

Cllr Bulge said he would so rule. He could not for the life of him see how Cllr Nepworth had acted with impropriety. So he had stocked up on nun dolls, so what? The Pope was not a nun. Cllr Bulge himself, speaking as one who tried to scrape a living as a retail newsagent and confectioner when the burden of office permitted it, made no secret of the fact that he had ordered large supplies of St Christopher key rings, novelty prayer books and Vatican snowstorm paperweights. Again, so what? Cllr Potter sold ice-cream, and all honour to him. Was Cllr Potter trying to say that he had no intention of cashing in on the Papal visit, should one take place, and that he would keep his Tonibell van locked in the garage until His Holiness had returned to Rome?

Cllr Arkwright said that talking of Rome, what was wrong with a twin-town arrangement between the Holy City and Clogthorpe? It was just a thought, but it might come off. It would strengthen the borough's hand when extending the invitation to the Pope. It was the chairman's mentioning Rome that had put the idea into Cllr Arkwright's head. It had just come to him out of the blue.

Cllr Bulge said that if Cllr Potter had quite finished chuntering to himself, the idea was certainly worth following up. Cllr Arkwright had made a constructive suggestion, which was more than could be said of some people, naming no names.

On a point of procedure, Cllr Nepworth asked if they were not getting into a chicken-and-egg situation. In other words which should come first—the invitation to the Pope, which would lend weight to the application for twin-towning; or the twin-towning invitation, which would lend weight to a possible visit by the Pope?

Cllr Bulge said it was not a matter that could be decided without further investigation. He would ask someone to propose an exploratory visit to Rome by the Parks, Recreation Grounds and Leisure Committee.

Cllr Potter said it was now quite clear to him that a quick skive to Rome on the ratepayer's money was what this debate had been leading up to.

The motion, that this committee do adjourn to Rome on a four-day Jet-saver working Winter Break, and that

Cllr Potter can always do the other thing, was passed overwhelmingly.

Prince of Wails

The First Official Biography

'The baby' – as His Royal Highness Prince William Arthur Philip Louis is affectionately known within his circle of close friends – is perhaps the most informal and relaxed of all the members of the Royal Family. His nanny is not even required to knock when she enters his private apartment. Nor are curtseys and bows demanded from the servants who open the door for the young Prince's pram when he goes for his daily walk. But woe betide those who take advantage of the absence of pomp and ceremony to become over-familiar: He is capable of quelling them with a dribble.

The story is told of a presumptuous nurse who, without waiting to be presented, bent over the Royal cot and gushed: 'Oo's a booful boy, den? Eh? Oo's a booful boy?' To the wretched girl's confusion The Baby blew an enormous, silent bubble. The message was clear. The nurse will not forget in a hurry that the correct mode of address should have been: 'Oo's a booful Royal Highness, den? Eh? Oo's a booful Royal Highness, sir?'

Yet to outsiders of lowly background who may be overawed in the presence of a future King of England, The Baby is compassionate. A gurgle puts them at their ease, whereupon a wave of a tiny foot may invite them to tickle the Royal toes. The ice broken, The Baby will often hold out his arms to be picked up. But this is discouraged by his retinue, some of whom are of the old school which believes that commoners may harbour 'germs'. The Baby, impatient of what he regards as fuddy-duddy protocol, does not hesitate to make his feelings known in no uncertain manner when his private detective stands in the way of a member of the public wanting to lift him out of his pram.

Sources close to the cot say that The Baby is absentminded, often forgetting his own name, and unable to concentrate. He never reads, shows no interest in politics, and does not go to the theatre. But he has a razor-sharp mind and a keen eye for the smallest detail. Princess Diana has been telling friends of the day he was entertaining some guests when, with the characteristic abruptness that is sometimes mistaken for rudeness by those who do not know him, The Baby began to scream. Alone among the distinguished company of experienced parents, trained nurses and vigilant detectives, the perceptive Baby had noticed that he was lying on his rattle.

Because The Baby fulfils no official engagements and does not have a career, preferring instead to fill his days being taken to feed the quack-quacks or sucking his teething-ring, he has been dubbed 'The Playboy Prince' by unkind critics who know nothing of his daily routine. The Baby is known to be hurt by such barbs. Close friends point out that he rises as early as five and puts in as full a day as he can, but such is his position that many of his intended activities are vetoed by well-meaning advisers. For instance, The Baby (who inherits the Royal Temper) is known to have been furious upon being told that to crawl up the nursery chimney was 'not on' for the future King William.

His surplus energies continue to worry The Baby's advisers who have been unable to convince him that he should relax whenever his duties permit. Such is his Royal Streak of stubbornness that the tactful hints that he might like to go bye-byes often have the opposite effect to that desired, and he remains awake and alert. A keen practical joker, The Baby has been known to put his restlessness to droll use by waking his nanny at two a.m.

A lifelong teetotaller and non-smoker, The Baby has simple tastes in food. He usually dines quietly on milk and strained spinach, with perhaps a little apple purée to follow. But although he eats little he likes his meals often and fusses when they are unpunctual. A firm traditionalist, The Baby has reintroduced to the Royal luncheon table a custom once observed by Henry VIII. If a dish displeases him, he spits it out.

Potential hostesses should note that The Baby never eats curry.

Although he has a large wardrobe of bibs, The Baby shows little interest in clothes, and unlike other members of the Royal family is never seen in uniform. He more often than not wears a long dress, but confidantes predict that this is only a passing phase. A shrewd judge of what suits his own easy-going personality best, he is expected to develop a taste for rompers.

Despite snide reports in gossip columns, there is no rift between The Baby and Princess Anne, although there is certain coolness between him and Captain Mark Phillips, due perhaps to their lack of common interest. The Baby does not particularly like gee-gees and Mark is not very keen on rusks. Like Captain Mark Phillips, The Baby finds it difficult to strike up a conversation, and there have been long embarrassing silences during visits by Princess Anne and her husband when The Baby and Captain Phillips have sat sucking their thumbs for want of anything to say to one another.

*

Visitors who do not want to get on 'the wrong side' of The Baby are advised not to push wads of cotton wool into his ear. He hates it.

But the Baby is always affable to the Princess, and she to him. Rumours of a quarrel arose from The Baby's apparent indifference to Princess Anne's recent visit to America. But she now realizes that The Baby's staff had not kept him informed of the visit.

The Baby's education has so far been informal. While he does not pretend to be an academic, and has as yet no O-levels, he has pleasantly surprised his parents by his ability to learn. In his daily, and very rigorous, teddy-bear recognition class, in which he is required to respond with a split-second gurgle whenever Teddy is poked through the bars of his cot, he regularly scores the highest marks. Educationalists are impressed at The Baby's results which they say are normally those of a baby twice his age. Princess Diana, as a former nursery-school teacher who must take much of the credit for The Baby's brilliant exam record, is known to be delighted with his progress. But it is too early to say whether he will become a university lecturer while awaiting the responsibilities of the Throne.

The Baby thoroughly enjoys a good story. His favourite after-dinner anecdote concerns five pigs, one of which went to market, while the second one stayed at home, the third had roast beef, the fourth had none and the fifth cried wee-wee-wee all the way home. Close friends say that despite the *non sequiturs* of the story, and the weaknesses in the plot, The Baby never tires of hearing it. On a recent occasion however, The Baby turned purple while one of his house-guests was recounting the yarn for the fifth time. It became obvious to the flustered house-guest that The Baby's razor-sharp brain had spotted the inconsistency in the story, whereby the second pig is home already while the fifth pig is obliged to run there. Hurriedly, she switched to an account of Ipsy-wipsy spider climbing up the spout, whereupon The Baby beamed his satisfaction. Truly a right Royal Baby!

Workers' Playtime-and-a-Half

Workers' Playtime will return to Radio Two for one week in early October, from five factories . . . the nostalgic return is part of the BBC's 60th anniversary celebrations.

Daily Mail

Thank you, ladies and gentlemen, you're very kind, and now with your permission a little recitation, a little recitation entitled 'The Shooting of Dan McGrew'. Now a bunch of the boys were whooping it up in the Malamute Saloon—

I say I say I say!

Yes yes yes, what is it? Can't you see you're interrupting my recitation?

My dog has no nose.

Your dog has no nose? Tell me, how does he smell?

Like the canteen rissoles.

Like the canteen—? You silly little man, you can't wander in here after all these years still claiming that your dog smells like the canteen rissoles! This is 1982, not 1942!

Is it?

It most certainly is, and this splendid assembly plant we're privileged to be visiting today doesn't have anything so common as a canteen.

Doesn't it?

No it does not, and even if it did, this splendid workforce you see before us here this lunchtime wouldn't put up with anything so common as rissoles. So when I say to you in future, 'Tell me, how does he smell?' you should reply, 'Like the staff restaurant vol-au-vents.' Ladies and gentlemen, I really am truly sorry for that disgraceful interruption. A bunch of the boys were whooping it up in the Malamute Saloon—

I say I say I say!

What is it now, you tiresome individual?

Do you know how many people work here?

No, I should be very interested to hear. Tell me, how many people work here in this very fine modern factory unit?

About half of them.

I don't wish to know that! Now look here, you opprobrious nincompoop—

My brother used to work here, you know.

Oh, did he? Then he was a very fortunate fellow. Tell me, what happened?

The shop steward caught him at it.

Now this has gone far enough! Don't you realize that times have changed since you last walked in here wearing that ridiculous headgear?

Have they?

They most certainly have, and these ladies and gentlemen haven't given up their rest period this morning to hear you making offensive remarks about shop stewards, workshy skilled labour, canteens, rissoles, or any of the rest of your insensitive claptrap. Now kindly leave the stage and allow me to continue with my recitation. A bunch of the boys were whooping it up in the Malamute Saloon, and the kid that handles the music box was hitting a ragtime tune—

I say I say I say!

Now what's the trouble, you ridiculous personage?

Are you putting it about that I'm barmy?

Barmy? Barmy? You can't barge into this very fine recreational facility using language like that!

Can't I?

Not in this day and age, my friend. 'Barmy' is hardly a term of approbation.

One of the storekeepers has done that.

What's that?

A term of probation.

That's not what these ladies and gentlemen have come to hear, and furthermore any unfounded accusations against that unfortunate storekeeper are no laughing matter, as the works disciplinary committee which decided to take no further action will be the first to tell you. Now pay attention, you ignorant specimen. If you wish to accuse me of spreading rumours concerning your psychoneurotic condition, you don't say, 'Are you putting it about that I'm barmy?'

Don't I?

You most emphatically do not. You say, 'Are you putting it about that I have a long history of mental disturbance?' Now be off with you and allow me to entertain these ladies and gentlemen. Back of the bar, in a solo game, sat Dangerous Dan McGrew—

The works manager's mother-in-law, the works manager's mother-in-law!

Yes yes yes, what about the popular works manager's

respected mother-in-law?

She's so mean, the works manager's mother-in-law is so mean, that when her old man swallowed a hundred aspirins she sent him out to get a headache.

That's not funny, that's not funny at all. Don't you realize that was a very sexist remark?

The girls in the typing pool like that.

The hard-working and very vivacious ladies in the typing pool like what?

Sex in the park.

Now look here, you're going to make me very cross if you carry on like this.

The works manager made me cross.

I'm sure that must have been a very unfortunate misunderstanding. Tell me, how did the popular works manager make you cross?

He made me cross the street so we wouldn't have to stop and talk to his mother-in-law.

You wretched ignoramus. Can't you see you're upsetting this wonderful audience with this tittle-tattle about the popular works manager's private affairs? Now we've all had enough of you so kindly remove yourself. Back of the bar, in a solo game, sat Dangerous Dan McGrew, and watching his luck was his light of love, the lady that's known as Lou—

He's a very heavy smoker, the works manager.

Is he indeed? Now there's a matter that *does* concern our wonderful audience here today. Doesn't the popular works manager realize that he should be setting an example? Doesn't he know that smoking may damage his health and could land him in hospital where all those wonderful doctors and nurses would have to lavish their wonderful care and attention upon him at the expense of more deserving individuals? Tell me, how many cigarettes a day does the popular works manager smoke?

Two a day.

Two a day? I thought you said that he was a heavy smoker?

Yes, he weighs nineteen stone.

That's quite enough of that!

From eating staff restaurant chip butties.

That will do!

You can't do it, you can't do it!

What can't I do, pray?

Put toothpaste back in the tube!

You think you're very clever, don't you? And watching his luck was his light of love, the lady that's known as—

The foreman's got two, the shop stewards have got two, but the staff restaurant manageress hasn't got any. What are they?

I really have no idea.

Bicycle clips.

Enough of this rudery. And watching his luck was his light of love—

The staff restaurant manageress has two, all the girls in the typing pool have two, but the works manager hasn't got any. What are they?

I'm sure I couldn't say.

You must need flaming glasses, then.

You absurd little man, what do you mean by coming in here and spoiling my act? Now kindly remain silent while I sing to this marvellous audience. And now, ladies and gentlemen a little song dedicated to all you good people here today entitled, She Was Only A Poor Little Matchgirl But She Knew When To Take Appropriate Industrial Action . . .

In the Dog-house

A series of nationwide seminars on the question of whether and how to allow council tenants to keep pets got off to a spirited start in London yesterday when more than forty local housing officers and animal lovers convened to discuss guidelines on ownership. The Joint Advisory Committee on Pets in Society, whose members include the Association of Metropolitan Authorities, veterinary associations, animal welfare groups, and trade organizations, has calculated that a third of all families live in local authority housing, and half of those families keep pets.

The Times

Mr Chairman, arf. Please allow me to express my gratitude for the opportunity to woof at this seminar today.

Mr Chairman, I would stress that I am appearing before you in my personal capacity as an Old English Sheepdog, and not as vice-chairdog of the Canine Community Relations Council. The Council's views will be expressed, I'm sure pungently enough, by our chairanimal Trixie when she returns from the vet's.

If I may, so to bark, present my credentials, Mr Chairman, I am Rover out of Kensington Champion and Rosamund of Chertsey, a Cruft's obedience winner and sometime President of the Bad Dogs Rehabilitation Scheme. In addition to my work in canine community relations I am, for my sins, joint chairdog of the Fido Memorial Research Project into the Needs of Dogs in an Urban Environment; a quarantine kennels Visitor; a member of the Dog-Food Consumers' Consultative Group; breed representative on the Advisory Committee on Doggy Calendars; and an honoury member of the Association of Welsh Corgis in Exile. For what it is worth, I am firmly of the opinion that dogs in public life should maintain an apolitical position and I make no apology for having put my pawmark alongside those of twelve distinguished moderate dogs and bitches from all walks of life on the

210

letter to *Our Dogs* which exposed the Puppies Against Barbara Woodhouse Action Committee as a front for the Mongrel Tendency.

In my voluntary work, Mr Chairman, I have supervised social adjustment clinics, day centres for the frisky, and ball-fetching therapy workshops on several council housing estates. I have thus had ample opportunity to sniff dogs of all breeds, though predominantly of the non-pedigree classes. When I return to my comfortable basket at night and think of some of the cases of distress and hardship that have been brought to my attention, Mr Chairman, I am not ashamed to say that I sometimes weep. Raow! Mr Chairman. Raoow! Raooooow! Raoooooooooooooooooooo-wowow! Raooooooo! Raoooooooooooooooooooooooooo-oooooowowowowowowowow!

Let me quote just three examples, from the caseload of my friend Pal, a dedicated Labrador who single-pawed runs canine community services for the whole of Lambeth. Tibbles (not his real name) is a deprived collie residing in a block of council flats. Five years old, Tibbles has never seen a postman. The number of times he has been taken to the park may be counted on the paws of six legs. He is taken out briefly each morning and evening to perform his ablutions, unless it happens to be raining when he is expected to do it in the lift like the tenants; however, consequent upon the last remaining saplings on the estate being uprooted by vandals he has contracted a kidney infection caused by retention of urine. Not surprisingly, this unfortunate collie has developed anti-social tendencies, for the only real exercise he gets is chasing the old-age pensioner he lives with round and round the living room. What is really needed for Tibbles and other under-privileged dogs on the estate is an adventure toilet provided by the council, with back-up from a support team who will take them walkies. But the funds for such a programme simply do not exist.

Next I come to Dobbin, as I shall call him, and whose breed shall we say is X Russell. Dobbin, in a caring society, would be in a home for disturbed dogs. Instead he has to live out his days on a housing estate where pets are strictly forbidden. The effect on him has been traumatic. Not only is he regularly shut in a laundry basket when council officials are in the offing, but each Friday, before the rent collector calls and perforce spends some time on the premises having his attention drawn to rising damp, fungus growths in the wardrobes and so on, Dobbin is dressed in infant's clothes, dumped in a pram with a Marmite-dipped dummy in his mouth and passed off as a baby. Worse: the absurd costume he is regularly forced to wear happens to be that of an infant of the female sex. There is a real fear that as a result of these experiences Dobbin may make medical history as the first transvestite dog. His predicament is heartbreaking. Social worker dogs wishful of investigating the conditions under which Dobbin has to live have had buckets of water thrown over them. But they have seen enough to make them deeply concerned about what society has done to this once outgoing and friendly X Russell.

Finally, Mr Chairman, I would refer you to the tragic case of twenty-six Beagles whom I shall identify only as A, B, C, D, E, F, G, H, I, J, K, L, M, N, O, P, Q, R, S, T, U, V, W, X, Y, and Z, a once close-knit nuclear family, most of them puppies, destined to be cruelly separated by a combination of cramped and insanitary living conditions and bureaucratic insistence, without regard to their needs, on strict adherence to outmoded rules and regulations. Instead of humanely transferring their owner to a block of larger flats (or even half a block if space was at a premium) where they could live as a unit, the council insisted on using its powers to break up the family. The consequences were tragic. A, D, H, P, R, T, U and V were sold on Club Row and our overburdened care service has lost contact with them.

B, F, K, M, N, W and Y were found homes even more cramped than the one from which they had been evicted, yet when they complained about their conditions, they were cuffed and shouted at. C, G, I, J, L, O, Q, S, X and Z, were taken into care by the Battersea Dogs' Home. E, when last heard of, was suffering the torment of living in a big house overlooking Richmond Park where he is allowed to look at the deer but not to chase them, on pain of being put back on his lead. When I see what an unthinking system has done to his family, Mr Chairman, it makes me really angry. Grr, Mr Chairman. Raff! Raff raff raff raff raff raff raff raff!

Mr Chairman, what is to be done? If dogs are to take their proper place in the community and to make that contribution to society which they are ready and able to give for little more than a pat and a marrow bone, it is not enough that local authorities must be compelled to encourage the keeping of pets on pain of a heavy fine. Not enough that there must be a code of behaviour for council tenants and others having the custody of dogs, with guidelines on what constitutes proper nourishment, exercise and recreation. Not enough that pettifogging rules imposing restriction of movement within housing estates and blocks of flats must be swept away, that all inner and outer doors must be equipped with dog-flaps, that perimeter fences surrounding coke compounds and rubbish dumps must be torn down, that boys throwing stones at dogs should be taken away in a van.

Mr Chairman, there must be an infrastructure of coordinating committees representing the interests of the dog, acting at national, regional and local level and responsible to a governing body with a supervisory role underpinned by statutory powers. Under the umbrella of such a network of committees, Mr Chairman, voluntary organizations such as the canine care services, the kennel improvement co-operative associations, the dog-fight supervisory councils, and like-minded concerned groups not forgetting those existing at tree-roots level such as the buried-bone collectives and street-happening experimental workshops, would pool their resources and expertise. Standing sub-committees would prepare consultative documents and working papers which would be submitted, for appropriate action, to a two-tier council of dogs made up at the inferior level of representatives from the co-ordinating committees, and at the superior level from the best of breed in the various counties. Within this framework—

Arf, Mr Chairman, arf! Arf arf arf! I fear you are finding these technicalities wearisome, Mr Chairman. As an alternative to the proposals I have been outlining, how would you feel if I just came up there and bit you in the leg?

The Road to Bradford Pier

A London travel tour operator is about to launch package holidays to Bradford for the 1981 summer season. For £90 a week people will get full board and lodging and four coach excursions.

Guardian

There, far below, is the flashy backbone of England, the Pennine Leisure Park. At first, the whole neon-lit length of it, from the Peak mobile home complex to Cross Fell Garden Centre, is visible. Then the Derbyshire all-year-round ski-slopes and the Cumberland hang-gliding school disappear, for you are descending, somewhere about the middle of the range, where the four-star Good Companions Hotel ('Nobbut middling' – Egon Ronay) thrusts itself between the holiday resorts of Yorkshire and the gambling strips of Lancashire. There is a glitter of water here and there, from the moorland tarns that are now called lidos. In summer you could wander here all day, listening to the

214

transistor radios, and never meet a soul except for the rest of your coach-party, half a dozen package tours from Germany and Holland, a few hot-dog vendors and ice-cream salesmen, and the official guidebook sellers dressed up as Brontës.

Down there are thousands and thousands of caravans, coaches, private cars and motor-cycles, most of them heading for the M62 slip-roads that lead into the town there in the narrow valley running up to the moors. It must be Bruddersford, for there, where the biggest of the NCP car parks nestles, is the Holiday Inn, and over there where Lane End Congregational Chapel used to be, is the Tourist Information Centre with its famous clock that plays all the Top Thirty in rotation.

Yes it is Bruddersford. Over there is the Space Invaders video-machine arcade, formerly Messrs Holdsworth's textile mill. The roof of the planetarium glitters in the sun, and not very far away is another glitter from the glass roof of the old Market Hall, where, securely under cover, you may roller-disco all day on fluorescent wheels.

Something queer is happening in that narrow thoroughfare to the west of the town. A red-blue-green-brown-beige tide flows sluggishly down its length. It is a tide of Stetsons, sombreros, berets, fezzes, Tyrolean hats, sun-bonnets and straw boaters. These hats have just left the purpose-built West Bruddersfield Amenity Centre. Thirty-five thousand tourists have partaken in what most local men call 't' bingo'. Now they are edging towards 't' McDonald's' or 't' Kentucky Fried Chicken' or 't' Kebab Express'.

Somewhere in the middle of this tide of hats is one that is different. It is neither Stetson nor sun-hat but is flat, peaked, and has the words B'FORD COUNCIL LEISURE DEPT emblazoned along its brim. Its owner, Mr Jess Oakroyd, is a supply bingo caller, ready to dash at a moment's notice to any of the amenity complexes that ring the borough, whichever may radio-call the

Director of Tourism's office that they are 't' short-handed'. Jess lives almost in the shadow of two strip-clubs, in a district known locally as 't' Naughty Square Mile', to be precise, at 51 t'Ogden Street. He is on his way there now, returning from a day's bingo-calling to his Saturday tea. He has walked this way, past 't' Golden Nugget', hundreds of times, but this Saturday is no ordinary day for Jess is on the threshold of great events.

As he moved slowly with the crowds he jostled an acquaintance who turned round, and, winking mysteriously as he pushed up his sunglasses, greeted him, 'Na Jess.'

'Na Jim,' This 'Na,' which must once have been 'Now', is the recognized salutation in Bruddersford. For pronunciation, see Hugo's *Teach Thiself Yorkshire*.

'Well,' said Jim, falling into step, 'what's tha' think on t' tourist season so far—'

'Neether nowt nor summat,' said Mr Oakroyd.

'Aye, it's neether one thing nor t'other,' agreed Jim. 'T' Americans hevn't showed oop, that's wheer t'trouble lies. Ahr Monica reckons on they're all flocking ower to t'Leeds this year. T'tale she's heard, they can get an all-in off-peak no-frills package – t'plane from t'New York, fo'teen days in t'Noil-comber's Arms an' all fahnd, a conducted tour rahnd t'abbatoir, an' a free ticket to t'Corn Exchange, an' still get change out on a five-pahnd note. T'Bruddersford can't top that, tha knaws, for all yon fancy amenity centres.'

''Appen not,' replied the taciturn Mr Oakroyd.

Changing the subject, Jim asked, ''Ow's that lad o' thine gerrin' on – him what's playing t'night shift in t'Pit Lane Desert Inn?'

'Our Leonard does tha mean? Neither muckling nor mickling,' grumbled Mr Oakroyd. 'He's nobbut second on t'bill, an' o'course, they on'y pay t'piecework rates, even to t'Frank Sinatra.'

'I've heard tell he's walking out wi' yon Directress o' t'Entertainment at t'Butlin's ower in t'Nuneaton,' pursued Jim. 'He wants to think on, tell him, if he's reckoning on gerrin' wed an' purrin' her up t'spout. Ther'll be short time in t'tourist business afore t'season's ower, if you ax me, an' if t'Desert Inn starts laying off he'll be in t'soup.'

"Appen,' said Mr Oakroyd.

'We've 'ad our teas,' remarked Mrs Oakroyd with satisfaction.

'Aye, so I see,' returned her husband gloomily, scraping the remains of a portion of Tandoori chicken on to his plate. 'Who fetched t'Nice'n'Spicy takeaway in?'

'Our Leonard. He's brought Albert Tuggridge wi' him.'

'An' what the hecky-thump's our Leonard doing 'ere at this hour?' demanded Mr Oakroyd aggressively. 'I suppose none o' t'customers dahn at t'Desert Inn wants to listen to a stand-up comic of a Saturday neet no more?'

'Leonard's done wi' t'Desert Inn,' announced Mrs Oakroyd. 'And not afore he gev t'manager a piece of his mind.'

'Getten t'sack, 'as he? An' what's he off to do now?'

'He's off to better himself,' said Mrs Oakroyd with triumph. 'Him an' Albert Tuggridge 'ave formed a double act an' they're off to top t'bill at t'Caesar's Palace, formerly t'Corporation Slipper Baths. Oh, an' Albert wants to knaw if he can come an' lodge wi' us.'

'Can he hummers like,' said Mr Oakroyd firmly. 'He can stop at t'Bus Station Hilton, t'same as all t'rest.'

Mr Oakroyd flung his peaked cap on the sofa and closed the door with a bang.

'Where have you been?' his wife demanded. 'Your dinner's been waiting for hours.'

217

'Been dahn to t'office,' answered Mr Oakroyd shortly. 'Ah've been stopped. Laid off.'

'You've been stopped? What on earth for?'

'For nowt!' cried Mr Oakroyd bitterly, 'T' bingo receipts is falling off, an' t'Director o' t'Leisure cracks on it's cos none o' t'foreigners can understand a blind word ah'm saying. So he gives me t'choice o'learning t'clickety-click an' t'legs-eleven in t'Spanish, t'Portuguese, an' t'German, else transferring to t'deckchair duties on t'Haworth Moor. "We've got to please t'tourist if we're to keep our 'eads above watter," he kept on saying. In t'end I told him I were sick to death o' t'tourism, an' then I walked out.'

Thin-lipped, Mrs Oakroyd said: 'An' t'Caesar's Palace has put all t'turns on short time. That settles it, Albert Tuggridge comes 'ere as t'lodger.'

'If Albert comes, I go,' said Mr Oakroyd and began packing.

'Go? Where to?'

'Down t'South to find work in t'mills.'

Autumn in Westminster

The House met at nine o'clock

MRS MOOCH asked if her husband had any plans to visit the House of Commons.

MR ARTHUR MOOCH: With permission. I should now like to answer that question. Parliament re-assembles next week and I shall be returning to London on Tuesday. (*Cries of 'Oh' and 'Da-da.'*) To this end, I propose to lay on the Table a list of requirements in the way of laundered shirts, dry-cleaned suits, and my dinner-jacket. Separate notice will be given as to toilet requisites.

MRS MOOCH: Is my right Hon Husband aware that he is the giddy limit? He has been mooning about this House for weeks, sucking his hollow tooth, straightening pictures and jingling the change in his pocket. He has had ample opportunity to make an announcement. Instead he waits until the eleventh hour before making his intentions clear, thus leaving those of us with a mandate to get the laundry and dry-cleaning done in an impossible position.

MR MOOCH: I am sorry if the Hon Wife has been inconvenienced but the date was published in *The Times*.

MRS MOOCH: I am grateful for that reply. Will my Right Hon Husband have regard to the fact that some of us never get a chance to read the bloody *Times*? For as long as we on this side of the House have known him, the Husband opposite has made it his policy to hog the bloody *Times* from breakfast onwards, yielding it up only long after dinner when he is too drunk to see straight, by which time it has been rendered indecipherable owing to the large number of intemperate, boring comments scrawled across its pages. Is he aware that as graffiti goes, observations of the order of, 'This does not accord with what the Minister told the Select Committee in February!' leave a lot to be desired?

MR MOOCH: I congratulate the Hon Wife on her gift for exaggeration and hyperbole, which continues to flourish as the green bay tree, unlike other of her attributes which may be said to be withering on the vine.

MRS MOOCH: Will my right Hon Husband accept some friendly advice? Will he pay attention to the truism that in public life it is almost as hazardous to mix one's metaphors as to mix one's drinks?

MR MOOCH: I am obliged. The Hon Wife's diatribe does not, however, disguise the position that unless drastic measures are forthcoming, those of us who have the remit and the responsibility to sit on this side of the House will be returning to Another Place with a suitcase full of dirty laundry.

THE BABY: Will the Right Hon Daddy state when he hopes to return home from that Other Place, and is it his intention to fetch me a Cubey Cube?

MRS MOOCH: *rose*—

MR MOOCH: Yes, I am aware what the Hon Baby means. The Hon Baby is not old enough for a Rubik Cube. (*Cries of 'Wah'*) The Hon Baby does not even know what a Rubik Cube is. It has read about the device in the papers, presumably—

MRS MOOCH: Though not *The Times*.

MR MOOCH: If the Hon Wife studied *The Times* with the same assiduity as the Hon Baby habitually tears that publication to ribbons before anyone has even glanced at it, I should not be in the humiliating position of facing my Parliamentary colleagues in baggy trousers. However, to revert to the Hon Baby's request. I refuse to pander passing fads and fashions by investing household funds in a Rubik Cube which would almost certainly become the most expensive building brick this House's nursery has ever seen, but I undertake, if the Hon Baby is good, to fetch it back some sweeties.

MRS MOOCH: The Hon Baby is deeply in my Right Hon Husband's debt. Will he now answer the first part of the Hon Baby's question and tell this House when he next proposes deigning to grace the House with his presence?

MR MOOCH: I must have notice of that question. Certainly not for two or three weekends. I have been neglecting my constituency of late – (*Cries of 'Neglecting Miss Thribley, you mean.'*) I will deal with the interruption if I may. Miss Thribley's name has been mentioned. I should like to place it on record in respect of Miss Thribley that while her loyalty, experience and expertise as my secretary are second to none, she is unfortunate enough to possess a face like a squashed melon. I appeal to the Hon Wife—

MRS MOOCH: Not with congealed egg on his chin, he doesn't.

MR MOOCH: I think I have the floor, particularly if the other side can only resort to cheap jibes. I ask the Hon Wife to recognize that had I ever wished to indulge in what I believe is known as a bit of the other while purporting to nurse my constituency, Miss Thribley would be the last—

MRS MOOCH: *rose—*

MR MOOCH: No, I will not give way. The Hon Wife has levelled an insinuation and I am replying to it as best I may. To introduce Miss Thribley into a constituency positively bulging with mature female sociology students all of whom have read their Malcolm Bradbury and are reputed to be raving for sexual experience, would, I was about to say, not only be politically unwise and lay one open to the risk of exposure in the pages of a certain satirical journal, but would be a case of taking coals to Newcastle.

MRS MOOCH: We are not talking about taking coals to Newcastle. We are talking about taking coals to the Splendide Hotel, Brighton. Perhaps my Right Hon Husband would care to make a statement about that?

MR MOOCH: The Hon Wife will have to provide more information about the matter on which she seeks enlightenment. If she is referring to last October's Party conference—

MRS MOOCH: I am referring, as my right Hon Husband perfectly well knows, not to last October's Party conference but to this June's so-called emergency meeting with his constituency committee. How does he explain a hotel bill for £174 plus VAT from a resort two hundred miles south of the Clogthorpe Arms where he claimed to be staying? Or has the Boundary Commission enlarged his constituency? Perhaps it was in the bloody *Times* and we on this side of the bloody House missed it?

MR MOOCH: The Hon Wife must not allow her tongue to run away with her. Rhetoric is a good servant but a bad master.

MRS MOOCH: But is Miss Thribley a good mistress?

221

That is what we are waiting to hear.

MR MOOCH: The Hon Wife puts questions and then will not wait for the answers. An hotel bill has been mentioned. The Hon Wife, though lacking the courage to admit it, has been going through the pockets of my brown suit.

MRS MOOCH: If my Right Hon Husband will yield for a moment. I was emptying the pockets before taking it to the cleaner's.

MR MOOCH: Then it is a pity, if I may say so, that that particular mission was not in the event completed.

MRS MOOCH: He is lucky I did not throw the suit into the boiler. He has yet to explain the hotel bill.

MR MOOCH: I am coming to the hotel bill, if the Hon Wife will bear with me. It is a forgery, planted by certain elements in my constituency – I will not name names, the Hon Wife has heard me mention them many times – with the aim of. discrediting me and perhaps driving me into the arms of the Social Democrats. (*Cries of 'Not to mention the arms of Miss Thribley.'*) But I say this to the House, and I say it with all the force at my command. Nothing, not the efforts of a minority of extremists, not forged hotel bills, not the vociferous Wife opposite, will persuade me to veer from that path which I have taken. Let us therefore hear no more of these wild accusations and counter-accusations that are pulling this House apart, but let us instead resolve to work together, as a team, and let us for God's sake get some buttons sewn on my shirt while there is yet time.

MRS MOOCH: Is my right Hon Husband aware that he takes the biscuit, that he really does?

MRS MOOCH: The Hon Wife is typically generous in her praise. If she has finished her breakfast perhaps I may be persuaded to draw attention to the state of my dinner-jacket?

THE BABY: The Hon Teddy would like to ask a question. The Hon Teddy wants to know if the Hon Daddy has

222

kissed Miss Thribley?

MR MOOCH: The Hon and gallant bear opposite is out of order, and the Hon Baby is looking for a smack-bottom.

The House rose at 9.45 am.

The Man Who Has Everything

These are worrying times for the Man Who Has Everything. He fears that the way things stand with those loved ones who normally put his name on their Christmas list, with a question mark beside it followed by '(Try Asprey's)' in brackets, he may finish up this year with Nothing. Or with a scarf, which would be worse than Nothing.

Accordingly the Man Who Has Everything rang me on his replica French antique candlestick telephone, and having found a free hour in his personalized pigskin diary-cum-credit-card-case-cum-miniaturized-A-Z-of-London-with-folding-magnifying-glass, invited me to discuss his apprehensions over drinks. It is a long time since I have had ice-cubes in my cocktail the shape of my host's initials, and made of Malvern water at that, so I accepted.

I found him fondling an onyx worry-egg in one hand and abstractedly playing his bathroom fruit-machine with the other. He was obviously deeply concerned. He asked me if I would like a gold swizzle-stick in my vodka martini. Had he been easy in mind he would not have committed a solescism like that: the martini would have been served ready-garnished with an olive speared on a silver cocktail-stick bearing the crest of the Worshipful Company of Digital Watchmakers.

He set the lead-crystal goblets down on limited-edition Bicentennial coasters depicting, respectively, the Boston Massacre and the surrender at Yorktown. He offered me a cigarette from a box that played a few bars of 'Greensleeves' quite prettily, pushed a bowl of monogrammed book-matches towards me, and indicated that the large commemorative medallion of Oliver Cromwell (one of twelve in the series 'Makers of British History') should be used as an ashtray.

We said nothing for some time. The Man Who has Everything toyed moodily with one of those contraptions where you activate a series of steel balls on the end of wires. I found myself quite hypnotized by an aquatic perpetual-motion device where the water changed colour as the glass tube tilted this way and that. Eventually, he reached for a sheet of 'Street Cries of Old London' writing paper from a tooled leather notelet-dispenser in the form of a very large dice, and did some sums on one of his pocket calculators.

'If my friends and relatives are to be believed, and my calculations are correct,' said the Man Who Has Everything, 'they have a sum total of £360 to spare for Christmas presents this year, or an average of twelve pounds apiece.'

'Times', I said, accepting an anchovy on toast from a pewter salver engraved with a likeness of Gypsy Moth II, 'are hard.'

'Harder than you know,' my host said, staring crossly at the twelve-foot teddy-bear he uses as a bulletin board. (He sticks party invitations to its chest with enamelled mapping pins.) 'You have not taken inflation into account. Twelve pounds these days will not even buy a gold money-clip converted from a Louis XIV five-franc piece.'

'I thought you already had a gold money-clip converted from a Louis XIV five-franc piece?'

'I don't have a spare one, though. In any case, I had in mind my Aunt Laura, who as well as not being imaginative has a bad leg and doesn't like trailing up and down New Bond Street for weeks on end. It would have saved her trouble.'

'That's very thoughtful of you,' I said.

'I think of them, but do they think of me?' the Man Who Has Everything grumbled. 'They *know* I lost a pair of monogrammed cuff-links last autumn. They *know* I'm still using last year's Colibri lighter. One gives them hints and all one gets for one's pains is a concerted whine about bank managers, mortgages and final demands for the rates.'

'Perhaps they mean to surprise you,' I comforted him. 'After all, twelve pounds can still buy a very nice executive toy.'

'Don't *want* executive toys,' sulked the Man Who Has Everything. 'Got lots of executive toys for my birthday, earlier this month.' His expression grew happier as he added, 'And a new chrome shaving mirror, and *The Times Atlas of the World*, and the compact edition of the *Dictionary of National Biography*, and an antique penny-in-the-slot weighing machine, and some more digital watches, and a woodblock of my initials from an old printing works, and some glass paperweights, and a subscription to the Fruit-of-the-Month Club, and a reproduction Tiffany desk-lamp, and four new address-books. Oh, and a Bangladesh famine Relief Fund Silver Bowl in a strictly limited edition of 2,000 designed and created by distinguished craftsmen which in every sense is an investment for life. It's in the boot-cupboard.'

'You did pretty well,' I said.

'No I didn't, I was in America at the time so I only got airmail parcels from people who knew my address. Some of them still owe me presents.'

'Perhaps they intend to give you something extra-special for Christmas and birthday combined. Although,' I admitted, 'it's difficult to see how they can make much of an effort on a sum of only twelve pounds each.'

The Man Who Has Everything picked up a table cigarette-lighter in the shape of a golf-ball, a Hallowe'en present from a man he had once shared a cab with. He flicked it on and off unhappily. The gloom was upon him once more.

'You don't know the half of it,' he said. 'The twelve pounds isn't only for me. It's all they have to spare for *all* their presents, so they claim. They've got to buy oven gloves for people who don't have Everything, packets of fibre-tip pens for the kids, that sort of thing. I'll be lucky if they have a fiver each left over for a set of giant brass paper-clips or a magnetic chess set.'

He poured more vodka martinis, absently tapping his foot in tune with the music as the cocktail-shaker played *Another Little Drink Won't Do Us Any Harm.*

'I feel very sorry for you in your plight,' I said, waving away the offer of Beluga caviare on Ritz crackers, 'but I'm not sure in what way you think I can be of help. You know already that I intend to give you a rare addition to your collection of moustache cups for Christmas; it is one that belonged to Mussolini and pretty well unique in that he was clean-shaven. I am afraid that is as far as I can go.'

The Man Who Has Everything took out a crocodile-skin wallet, looked inside it, consulted a second crocodile-skin wallet from another pocket, and handed me a slip of paper.

'This is a list of all the friends and relatives who are honour bound to give me Christmas presents. I want you to explain my situation and persuade them, where you can, to take out over-drafts.'

'I will do my best,' I said. 'But you must realize that money is very expensive these days, and many of your friends are feeling the pinch.'

'Are there no workhouses?' demanded the Man Who Has Everything. 'Do your best for me.'

'I will,' I assured him, rising to leave. 'But you must remember that it is no use asking for the moon.'

The face of the Man Who Has Everything lit up. It was a pleasure to see such childlike, fleeting happiness.

'You said that, I didn't.'

Blowing in the Wind

Confidential files from a probation office were found in
a wood by a man walking his dog. The files, from
Northampton's probation office, are believed to have
been mistakenly put in a rubbish sack and blown into
the nearby woods. Security has been tightened.

Daily Mirror

From Director of Leisure to Superintendent of Amenities: I have had a complaint from the team-leader of the Bog Lane Leisure Centre Kids' Nature Project that on a mushroom-gathering field-trip to the King George V Memorial Plantation recently, confidential files from the probation office outnumbered mushrooms in the ratio of twelve to one. Many of these files concerned members of the project. Your comments please.

From Superintendent of Amenities to Director of Leisure: There should have been far more mushrooms available than that. I suspect that unauthorized visitors are making free with council fungi and I have written to the Gypsy Liaison Officer to ask if he can shed light on the matter. Meanwhile I am arranging for the King George V Memorial Plantation to be surrounded by barbed wire.

D of L to S of A: It was not the paucity of mushrooms I was calling into question, but the plentitude of confidential probation reports. What were they doing in our plantation?

S of A to D of L: Oh, I see. They blew there.

D of L to S of A: Where from?

S of A to D of L: Gasworks Street adventure play-ground.

D of L to S of A: Were these documents part of a kids' creative workshop project, then, or what?

S of A to D of L: Not exactly. As you know, the implementation of staff cuts as required by Government policy has left our amenity litter-collection resources overstretched to the point of near-breakdown. I have warned your Directorate of this time without number.

The reason the confidential probation reports were blowing about the Gasworks Street adventure playground was that all my available litter-collection staff were engaged in picking a quantity of maximum-security prison records out of the rhododendron bushes.

D of L to S of A: We will come to the prison records in the rhododendron bushes in due course. All I want to know for the present is how the probation reports came to be in the adventure playground in the first place.

S of A to D of L: My information is that it was an administrative error.

D of L to S of A: Yes, I thought it might be. Whose?

S of A to D of L: Owing to an absence of adequate supervision consequent upon the running down of staff levels in accordance with the requirements of Government policy, six bin-liner sacks of confidential probation reports were delivered to the adventure playground warden by mistake. He had indented for six bin-liner sacks of horse-chestnuts.

D of L to S of A: Why?

S of A to D of L: To give deprived inner-city children conker experience.

D of L to S of A: I don't wish to know that. The question I am asking is how we came to deliver these six bin-liner sacks of confidential probation reports in error. What were they doing in our possession?

S of A to S of L: They were stored, along with the chestnuts we had collected for adventure playground use, at the back of the administrative building in the Robin Hood Forest picnic area.

D of L to S of A: Any chance of finding out why, bearing in mind the manpower shortages of which you so frequently and eloquently complain, we should be acting as surrogate filing cabinets for the county probation service?

S of A to S of L: It was only a temporary arrangement. Once we were able to divert our limited litter-collection force to retrieving the rest of the missing documents, we intended to return them to the probation service with our compliments. You will appreciate that searching 5,600 acres of dense woodland is a formidable task, especially with our depleted resources. But I expect you are anxious to know how approximately a quarter of a tonne of confidential papers came to be strewn about the forest?

D of L to A of A: Yet, if it is not too much trouble.

S of A to S of L: I blame the deer. They came down to the picnic area, upturn the litter baskets, and scavenge about in the discarded papers which are then left to blow far and wide. I am considering, subject to our current budgetary restrictions, having the litter baskets cemented to the ground.

D of L to S of A: Meanwhile, who left a quarter of a tonne of confidential probation reports in the picnic area litter baskets?

S of A to S of L: The probation officers themselves. They were on their annual picnic.

D of L to A of A: So we are not the only people to suffer the pestilential Government cuts. The probation officers are so overworked that they have to catch up with their paperwork on what should have been a jolly and relaxing staff outing.

S of A to S of L: Not quite. These were old reports. They had their sandwiches wrapped up in them.

D of L to A of A: This is scandalous. And they weren't even shredded?

S of A to S of L: No, thought I understand the cucumber was very thinly sliced.

D of L to A of A: The files, you idiot.

S of A to S of L: Oh, the files! No, thank God. Have you ever tried extracting a shredded confidential file from a young conifer? It is like picking up confetti. Until recently, it was standard practice for bin-loads of shredded documents to be dumped on open spaces and other amenity areas without our control with no regard for the retrieval problems involved. However, since that business with the Ministry of Defence when I had to switch my entire litter-collection squad from picking up Area Health Authority reports on the common, to go careering up and down the canal bank looking for spaghetti-thin slivers of top secret bumph relating to the Cruise Missile, I have persuaded most departments and authorities handling sensitive material to leave it unshredded when disposed of. It makes our work that much easier, as I pointed out in a confidential circular.

D of L to S of A: Yes, I know, I found a copy of it on the golf-course. By the way, I hope your staff are not so hard-pressed that those probation reports are still littering the King George V Memorial Plantation, which was where this exchange of memos started?

S of A to D of L: No, no, no. They were collected in one of our lorries and returned to the probation service offices yesterday, most of them.

D of L to S of A: In that high wind?

S of A to D of L: Normally, of course, we would have used a van, but owing to the stringent cutting-back of departmental vehicles due to—

D of L to S of A: Yes, all right, very well. Moving on now to those maximum-security prison records in the Silver Jubilee Park rhododendrons. Your comments, please.

S of A to D of L: Didn't you receive our very simple straightforward explanation of that particular isolated incident?

D of L to S of A: No. I am sure I would have remembered it if I had.

S of A to D of L: That's funny. I wrote you a long memo and was just in the course of signing it when it blew out of the open window. I assumed it would have reached you by now.

(The above correspondence was found under a gooseberry bush in the nursery-garden of the county remand home.)

Rattle of a Simple Car

Cars of the future will talk to their drivers, helping to
cut down accidents, scientists were told yesterday.
Professor Michael Hampshire of Salford University
said that the talking car might give information on
average speed, fuel consumption, distance covered and
estimated time of arrival.

Daily Telegraph

You are now travelling in excess of the maximum speed
permitted on the motorway.

You are now travelling in excess of the maximum
speed permitted on the motorway.

Oy! You got cloth ears or something? Bit Mutt and
Jeff this evening, are we? I said YOU ARE NOW TRA-
VELLING IN EXCESS OF THE MAXIMUM SPEED
PERMITTED ON THE THINGY. Motorway. I mean I
wouldn't mind, kidder, but we're only on the B flaming
2348.

That's better.

You are about to overtake a cyclist. Exercise caution.
Run the bugger down, that's what I'd do if you left it to
me. Think they own the bloody road.

You are approaching traffic lights set at red. Reduce
speed now and change down to third gear.

Continue to change down and halt within 30 yards.
Handbrake on.

Christ, I feel knackered today. I do. Absolutely
washed up.

You know what it is, don't you? Bloody carburettor.

The traffic lights have now changed to green. You
may select first gear, release the handbrake and pro-
ceed with caution. COME ON THEN, BERK!

And I mean to say, it's not as if you haven't had
proper notification about that carburettor, kidder. I
mean to say, what did I tell you 3418 miles back? I can
give you my exact words. Going up the A23 we were,
where them road works are. Where you nearly ran me
into the back of that milk float. Then we stalled. And I

said, stuff this for a game of candles, I said, you're supposed to fit a new air cleaner element every 12,000 miles (20,000 km) or earlier in dusty operating conditions, I said. You're completely out of order, I said, you shoulda done it three month back when I was in for servicing. And now look what we've got, I said. An exhaust manifold what looks like a pig's snout I said. Well don't blame *me* if I fail the flaming MOT, I said.

Don't you remember? Course you bleeding remember. Look, sunshine, if you're too bloody mean to pay a mechanic, why don't you do it yourself? Simply unscrew the wing nuts from the top of the cleaner, withdraw the cover, and discard the element. Are you listening? Thoroughly clean the container, fit a new element, refit the cover and wing nuts and bob's your uncle. Simple when you know how.

Your average speed is now 63 mph (101 km). How you manage to keep from getting nicked is something we shall never know.

Your estimated time of arrival at Ye Mayde of Kent Tavern and Quality Steak bar is eighteen forty-five hours. And if you intend getting pissed, either park me where you don't have to reverse to get out or better still phone for a mini-cab, because you trying to get into reverse gear when you've had a few, my son, is something painful to behold.

Looka this twit in front. Bleeding Jap job, ennit? Looka that steering. All over the place. You know what it is, doncha? They don't have big enough lubricating nipples on the swivel hub ball joints. So consequently – *watch this bloody motorbike, coming down the outside lane.* YOU MAD BUGGER YOU! WHATCHA THINK THE BLEEDING WHITE LINES ARE FOR? PLAYING TENNIS ON? Berk! – so consequently, they don't get enough grease so they what's-it-bloody-called, sieze up. I mean if you want my frank and honest opinion, I think these Japanese motors is rubbish. I think they shouldn't let 'em in. And another thing, you can't understand a bleeding word they're saying. It's like double Dutch.

You are now approaching the dual carriageway. Your fuel tank now contains precisely six gallons (27.276 litres). Oil level satisfactory. Sparking plug adjustment is advised.

Can you hear something rattling?

I bloody can. Your bloody door's not fastened properly, you daft pratt. Get it locked!

Stroll on! I've got to tell you every mortal thing, haven't I? It's like being out with a bleeding four-year-old. I mean to say, your offside indicator's only been flashing for the last fifteen miles – you haven't noticed, have you? It's always down to Joe Muggins. Well bubbles to it. Next time you leave that indicator on it can flash all bloody night as far as I'm concerned.

So who you meeting tonight, then? Is it her with the big ones? Bet it is. The one with the knockers. Cor! What? I know your game, you rascal. Top her up with gin, get a steak rammed down her throat, bottla wine, coupla brandies, all round to that lay-by we just passed, then a quick tremble in the back seat. Eh? Spota rumpoh? You're a crafty one!

I'll tell you what, tosh. You play your cards right and I'll do you a big favour. I will, I'll do you a big favour. Watch this van, he's going to turn right without signalling. YOU STUPID PRATT! HAVEN'T YOU GOT NO ARMS?

No, I'm serious kid. If you swear on your mother's grave that you'll be a good lad and get that new air cleaner element fitted, then I'll tell you what I'll do for you. While you're after her in the back seat, I'll sing.

I will, I'll sing. Because it turns them on, you know, does music. You ask any motor you like – Cortina, Rover, Jag, any motor what's big enough in the back – and they'll all tell you the selfsame thing. It gets them going.

So I'll tell you what: as soon as you start getting her

buttons undone, say something in code as a signal – like you could say: 'Stone me, it's flaming hot in here' – and I'll sing 'Gimme the moonlight'. She'll be raving for it after that, firm promise.

In this vicinity, beware of low-flying aircraft. In this vicinity, beware of low-flying aircraft. Gimme the moonlight, gimme the girl . . .

You didn't know I could imitate Frankie Vaughan, did you? Oh, I can do them all, tosh. Sammy Davis Junior, Al Jolson, Crosby, Eric Morcambe, Rolls-Royce, Ol' Blue-eyes, Arthur Askey. I thang yow!

See if you can guess who this is. Just like that! Heh-heh. Just like that!

You are approaching the end of the dual carriage-way. Reduce speed now. I'll give you another one. Who's this? Nevah! In the field! Of human thingy! Stone me, I had that off pat, one time. I'll be forgetting my own registration number next.

You have reached the end of the dual carriageway and must reduce speed. Play it again, Sam. You dirty rat! You are driving on the wrong side of a two-way highway and approaching an S-bend in excess of the maximum speed permitted on the motorway. Why don't you come up and see me some time, honey? Shut that door. Ooh you are awful but I like you. Unless you take immediate action you are going to crash into the oncoming sand-lorry. LEFT HAND DOWN, YOU DOZY SOD!

Bloody hell fire!

I've got some good news and some bad news for you, kidder. The good news is you don't have to worry about that new air cleaner element any more, and the bad news is you're bloody dead.

Just like that.

Nevah! In the field! Of human conflict!

Gimme the moonlight, gimme the girl . . .

Tech it from Here

The Open University's little brother, the Open Tech,
came into the world yesterday . . . Though it would
have the same open access policy as the Open
University and would borrow its distance-learning-
techniques, the Open Tech would be much strongly
oriented towards employers, and to the world of work
in general, it was stressed . . . It will concentrate on
providing training and retraining in technical skills.

Daily Telegraph

Good morning. And just to get us toned up before we
learn how to strip down a 16-line internal automatic
telephone exchange this morning, let's do some more
of those exercises we started last week with Muriel at
the piano.

In the crosslegged position now . . . screwdrivers
and working materials at the ready, and you should be
referring to the exercise chart in this week's *Radio Times*
or page 349 on Ceefax. *And* one and two and attach
angle Bracket B as shown in Fig 19 and solder. And rest.
And three and four and bore transverse holes in pivotal
coupling and apply bolts and collars. Deep breath, and
tighten lock-nuts. *And* five and six and sandpaper
rough edges. And stop there.

And as well as having thoroughly limbered up those
stiff muscles you should by now have built a stand for
your hi-fi system. In next week's keep-fit spot we'll
start building the hi-fi system itself but those of you
who are a little overweight do please check with your
doctor first. He may recommend you to build just a
straightforward audio amplifier.

And just while we're recovering our breath, I'd like
those of you who are studying chemistry to copy down
this complete table of all known chemical elements I'm
going to flash on your screens while Muriel gives us
another tune. Reading from left to right the table gives
the symbol of each particular element, then its name,
its derivations, its atomic number and weight, its spe-

cific gravity and its fusing point, and as you can see there are quite a few elements between actinium and zirconium so you'd better get your skates on. Those of you who aren't on the chemistry course can get on with the boilermaking exercises I gave you at the beginning of term, but if you happen to be in the same household as someone who *is* taking chemistry, a husband or wife perhaps, please make your boiler quietly.

All right, and if you'll put your chemistry notebooks and acetylene torches away now, you'll remember that in our last session we dismantled a Hawker-Siddeley aero engine and that should still be laid out neatly on your living-room floor. I'd like you please to grease all the parts if you will and then put them carefully aside for the time being because this week we're going to have a close look at a cross-section of your car. If you haven't already sawn the car in two please do it now as quickly as possible, lengthwise if you will, using an ordinary chainsaw or the appropriate attachment on your Black and Decker, and bring the nearside cross-section of car indoors. By the way, if any of you have been having problems with the floor caving in, there's a cement-infilling booklet you can send for.

Now while those of you who haven't yet sawn your cars in two are catching up with the rest of us, one of Open Tech's viewers in South Wales has sent in a mne-monic for remembering that rather tricky computer formula for the reduction of binary variable logical interconnections obtained by factoring of common terms, which should be down in your notebooks as $AC + AD + BC + BD = A(C + D) + B(C + D) = (A + B)(C + D)$.

And our viewer rather cleverly suggests that if you think in terms of fruit with A representing apple, B banana and so on, and the brackets also representing bananas, it's far far easier to remember the formula as apple cherry plus apple date plus banana cherry plus banana date equals apple banana cherry plus date banana plus banana banana cherry plus date banana equals banana apple plus banana banana and banana cherry plus date banana.

Thank you for a very handy hint, that South Wales viewer.

And one more tip. When distilling nitric acid either from rainwater or by catalytic oxidation of ammonia gas, try putting an old spoon in the mixture. When the spoon dissolves, your nitric acid is ready. And that little wrinkle comes from one of our housewife students in Dorset.

And a correction while we're waiting. In last week's recipe for bricks we unfortunately missed out one of the ingredients. You do in fact need straw as well as the various other things we mentioned. Sorry about that, bricklayers.

All right then, your cross-section of car should be in position by now and the intersected battery and engine should be on your right, or on your left if you drive a Volkswagen or any other foreign make of car with the engine in the back. And if I were you, I'd just pop a baking-tin under the section of battery to prevent acid from eating into your carpet. Oh, and by the way, I should have mentioned that this particular lesson doesn't cover commercial vehicles, so I'm sorry if any of you have sawn a van or lorry in half. Keep the piece though, because we'll probably get round to vans and lorries later in the term.

All right, now for this week's exercise I'm going to ask you to make a detailed blueprint of your cross-section of car and identify with arrowed numerals as many components as you can. Then solder the car together again but make sure you keep your blueprint in a very safe place because that's going to be the text for the car maintenance course we'll be embarking on as a little light relief between Aerodynamics Part II and Aerodynamics Part III, when, by the way, you'll be required to piece that aero engine together again and knock up a simple twin passenger monoplane, so don't let the cat play with any of those ballbearings and perhaps lose components you're going to need.

Elementary carpentry. You know, many students are still not clear how to put their front doors back on their hinges after those first steps in planing and beading we covered three or four weeks ago. I'm afraid re-hanging front doors isn't covered in the present syllabus but we are hoping to institute a house-building course next term, and obviously that will tell you all you need to know about front doors and more. So we'd ask you to be patient until then. Meanwhile, why not test your aptitude for the course by bricking up your doorway as a temporary measure?

Web-offset printing, quantity surveying, practical plumbing, first year machine-tool engineering and home coal-mining have, I'm afraid, had to be held over this week because our Open Tech Programme is running a little over schedule. We'll try to make up for that next time round.

And I haven't forgotten that we've still got that 16-line internal automatic telephone exchange to strip-down, and now's the time to disconnect your exchange from the mains so that you're not troubled with incoming calls from the bathroom or kitchen while destroying your data input switches. But let's turn first to television maintenance, and I want you to imagine that the screen I'm speaking to you on now has gone what in layman's language we would call on the blink. Now if you have your toolkit and spare tube of the appropriate size at the ready, we'll go through the checking process step by step. All right, now the first thing you must do, of course, is switch off your set, and I'll just give you a moment to do that . . .

Privy Council

Two senior council officers were wrongly disciplined for taking pity on an 83-year-old widow and decorating the ceiling of her home, an industrial tribunal was told yesterday.

They were moved to other jobs on lower salaries after complaints from officials of the Union of Construction Allied Trades and Technicians.

A council disciplinary hearing found that the men knew, or should have known, that the ceilings were 'blacked' because of a dispute.

Daily Telegraph

Minutes of special branch meeting, Slagton Boro' Maintenance Operatives Branch, Amalgamated Socy of Ragged Trousered Philanthropists.

Bro Kneape reported that he had had it up to here. He had had no satisfaction as regards the thingy, he had made representations at personnel officer level until he was blue in the face, and honestly, he was not lying, it was like talking to a brick bleeding wall. Bro Kneape gave up, he really did.

Bro Cooney said personnel officers, he had a four-year-old nipper what could fill the post better, he kidded branch meeting not.

Bro Ratchet said if bleeding Liver-sausage (Mr N. D. Liversedge, Co-ordinator of Personnel, Slagton Borough Council) called himself a perso-bleeding-nel officer, his (Bro Ratchet's) arse was a perso-bleeding-nel officer.

Bro Eames, on a point of procedure, asked if branch was dead sure the thingy was Liver-sausage's pigeon.

Bro Kneape said if Bro Eames could handle negotiations better than what they was being handled already, he (Bro Kneape) would be only too glad to chuck the job in there and then. You slaved your fingers to the bone (reported Bro Kneape), doing paper work and Christ knew what, then when you reported to branch, that was the bleeding thanks you got.

Bro Eames said he was only asking, there was no need for Bro Kneape to get the bleeding hump.

Branch chairman asked if branch meeting could be a bit more constructive.

Bro Kneape reported look, he had tried the Borough Engineer's Dept, he had tried the Borough Health Dept, he had tried Welfare. The Chief Executive, he had been down the Town Hall and had a go at him personal; and they had all told Bro Kneape the self-same bleeding thing. The thingy was Liver-sausage's pigeon. Definitely. No questions about it whatsoever in any shape or form.

On a point of information, Bro Tompsett asked if he could ask what the thingy was that Bro Kneape was making reference to, or was it supposed to be a closely-guarded secret which you had to belong to a certain clique before you knew what was going on.

Branch chairman asked Bro Tompsett to withdraw grossly offensive remark about cliques.

Bro Tompsett said that was funny, coming from branch chairman. Everybody knew what clique he was talking about. There was Bro Kneape, there was Bro Ratchet, there was Bro Cooney, and there was the branch bleeding chairman, and they was like that, the whole pack of them. They ran the branch like it was their own private bleeding club. However, he had been told to withdraw so he withdrew. He would still like to know what the thingy was when it was at home, if it was not too much trouble, pardon him for breathing.

Bro Kneape said that Jesus Christ, some mothers did have them. He thought everyone knew what the thingy was. It was the outside carsey at No 3 Gravel Depot. The bog. The toilet, as he expected Bro Tompsett would prefer to call it. If Bro Tompsett had ever come to meetings (continued Bro Kneape) he would know that demands for an inside jakes at No 3 Gravel Depot had been pursued at branch level till they was sick of hearing about it.

Bro Tompsett asked how, not being a bleeding conjuror, he could be expected to attend branch meetings on a regular basis when his wife was in dock with her leg. Perhaps Bro Kneape did not know what it was like to have four kids and get their tea ready. However, Bro Tompsett was straying from the point.

Branch chairman said too bloody true.

Bro Tompsett said the point was, what had the bleeding No 3 bleeding Gravel Depot to do with branch? They was all skilled painters and decorators, else they was plumbers, else they was electricians, else they was carpenters. One thing they was not, and that was Nigerian bleeding road-sweepers, what he believed had jurisdiction for filling the bleeding Council gravel bins. So (concluded Bro Tompsett) why should it matter a sod to branch whether No 3 Gravel Depot's carsey was outside, inside, or on the bleeding roof?

Bro Ratchet said that was right, pull the bleeding ladder up.

Bro Tompsett maintained that he had asked a straight question and was entitled to a straight answer.

Inviting Bro Tompsett to piss off, Bro Kneape said that he was an item of female anatomy. If Bro Tompsett would poke the wax out of his ears he would be aware that branch was supporting representations made at branch level by the Nat Union of Snowshifters. It was reciprocal. Branch supported the snowshifters' claim for an inside carsey at No 3 Gravel Depot, and the snowshifters would support any claim branch might make in the future, it might be a wage claim, it might be a turps allowances claim for getting paint out of their hair, it might be anything. Only that turd Liver-sausage did not want to know. Speaking in a personal capacity Bro Kneape said that he had had a bellyful.

Bro Cooney proposed that branch should stop frigging about and give Liver-sausage an ultimatum: either he got the snow-shifters' thingy implemented by Monday or it was industrial action.

On a point of order, Bro Tompsett asked why branch should take industrial action on behalf of snowshifters, when snowshifters was not taking industrial action themselves.

Bro Cooney said it was the principle, wasn't it?

Bro Gibbs said that he had taken full cognizance of all what had been said, and he was not knocking Bro Cooney's call for industrial action, the reverse in fact. Sod them, was what Bro Gibbs said. But branch had to take into consideration what the media would do with it. He could just see the headlines in *The Daily Telegraph*: 'COUNCIL WORKERS IN BOG STRIKE.'

Bro Kneape, through the chair, asked if he could ask Bro Gibbs one question and one question only. Was he in support of industrial action by a decision democratically arrived at, or was he going to be a blackleg all his life?

Bro Gibbs said that if Bro Kneape called him a blackleg he would knock his (Bro Kneape's) twatting head off. He would remind branch that he (Bro Gibbs) had taken part in more industrial action than Bro Kneape had had hot dinners. If Bro Kneape would listen for a bleeding change instead of shooting off his bleeding cakehole, he would know that all Bro Gibbs was saying was that there was industrial disputes and industrial disputes. Instead of all-out strike, thus taking wage-packets out of the mouths of wives and kiddies, what was wrong with a bit of selective action, nudge, nudge, wink wink, say no more?

Branch chairman asked Bro Gibbs what he was rabbiting on about.

Bro Gibbs said werl, what about No 17, Hugh Dalton Approach?

Branch chairman asked what a-bleeding-bout it?

Bro Gibbs said werl, he (Bro Gibbs) had a works docket, didn't he?

Branch chairman said so bleeding what, why didn't Bro Gibbs tell the branch something it didn't bleeding know. He (branch chairman) would bet he could tell Bro Gibbs what works docket it was, as well. It was that job he should have done two bleeding weeks ago:

242

replace cracked toilet, connect to waste pipe, seal, adjust to existing cistern, replace tiled surround where rotted or cracked, and make good.

Bro Gibbs said right then, what was wrong with not doing it?

Branch chairman said Bro Gibbs *hadn't* done it, that was the point he was trying to make.

Urging branch chairman to use his loaf, Bro Gibbs said that what he meant was, make it official. Black the leaking carsey at No 17 Hugh Dalton Approach until such time as Liver-sausage agreed to take decisive action as regards the carsey at No 3 Gravel Depot. If that wasn't poetic justice, Bro Gibbs did not know what was.

Bro Kneape said stone the bleeding crows, he would ask the secretary to delete from the minutes all he had said about Bro Gibbs, he was a bleeding marvel.

On a point of order, Bro Tompsett asked through the chair if Bro Gibbs happened to know who lived at No 17 Hugh Dalton Approach.

Bro Gibbs said he did not know, some old cow.

Bro Tompsett informed branch that it was his (Bro Tompsett's) mother.

Bro's Kneape, Ratchet, Cooney and Gibbs and the branch chairman concurred that that was it, that was all it wanted, talk about laugh, they (Bro's Kneape, Ratchet, Cooney and Gibbs and branch chairman) could have died.

On an overwhelming show of hands, branch recommended that leaking carsey at No 17 Hugh Dalton Approach do be blacked forthwith.

Across the River and into the Dole Queue

Kenya has decided to ban all hunting. The Government is prepared to lose £500,000 a year on the sale of hunting licences . . . Hundreds of thousands of dollars pour in, but it is only a fraction of the millions spent by package tour viewers and photographers.   *Financial Times*

It was hot coming down to the track where the Kodak stand sells colour film and next to it, in the shade, there is usually a woman selling postcards of rhino and buffalo.

I was glad the woman was not here today. I hated her guts. There was a time when I could not get near enough to the buff waterbuck for a good picture and I paid the woman fifty cents for two postcards of the waterbuck grazing and being eaten by a leopard. But if you went through the forest and down the mountain and followed the watercourse and the hilly slope of the land until the grass was brown and burned, you came to a kiosk where you could buy those same postcards for fifteen cents each.

'I do not forget such things,' I said to the woman.

The woman said, 'I have a living to earn. You earn a living and I do not complain. You are a writer, so they tell me. All you need is a pen, paper and what is in your head. If you were a taxidermist like my husband you would need not only your tools and the strength of your hands, but the carcass of a tiger.'

'There are no tigers in Africa,' I said.

'It is so long since I helped my husband insert glass eyes into the mounted head of an animal that I have forgotten,' the woman said. 'Such work is no longer allowed. My husband stuffed the cat, the dog and the budgerigar and then he shot himself.'

'You should have stuffed your husband and charged admission,' I said unkindly, hating the woman's guts. 'Twenty-five cents for a postcard is too much. I do not forget such things.'

'I have to earn a living,' the woman said.

The woman was not there in the shade of the Kodak stand today but in her place there was a white hunter selling matches from a tray.

We had seen gazelle that morning and I had a close-up of Kubu the rogue baboon in my Nikkon camera. Nobody else had that close-up. There would be cold German beer to drink and I had felt good as we came down to the track that leads past the Kodak stand to the

People's Dispensary for Sick Animals. I did not feel good when I saw the white hunter selling matches.

I sat on a petrol box with my back against a tree and spoke his name, which was Carl. After the Government stopped the hunting there was a time when Carl brought in a bull elephant from the plain behind the blue hills and it gave rides to children for a sum that Carl and the nannies of the children fixed between them. Everyone in the long bar of the Nairobi Bird-watchers' Club agreed the Carl had it made.

'What happened to the elephant, Carl?'

'It is now some ivory-backed hairbrushes, a rack of snooker balls and four umbrella stands. Old habits die hard and when a party of Americans made me an offer I let them hunt the elephant round the traffic island outside the Holiday Inn. The Government took away my money and put me in jail.'

'These are not good days for you, Carl.'

He shrugged.

'There are good days and bad days. I stand here with my tray of matches in the shade of the Kodak stand. There is shade for maybe three, four hours. It is cool. The matchboxes have a joke on the back. Sometimes passers-by are amused by the jokes and they buy my matches.'

He showed me the jokes on the backs of his matchboxes. These are the jokes as I remember them.

A man had a friend who was sick. He told no-one about his sickness but he lay in his room listening to the silk-worms eating the mulberry leaves and one night under the full moon he died.

The man did not know his friend was dead and he called at the house.

'Is Charlie in?' the man asked his friend's wife.

'Charlie died last night,' the woman said. She was red-eyed from weeping

'Did he say anything about a tin of paint?' the man said.

Another man met a friend in the street.

He said, 'I am going to the doctor. I do not like the look of my wife.'

'I will come with you. I hate the sight of mine,' his friend said.

I gave the matchboxes to Carl.

'These are terrible jokes, Carl. It is no work for a man, selling matches. Why won't you go up-country and open a sketching lodge, and then the Americans will come and make watercolours of the wildebeest?'

'They would want to turn the wildebeest into cushion covers,' Carl said. 'I would end up in jail again. I am better off selling matches.'

'It is no work for a man,' I said.

'No one could ever accuse you of not chewing your cabbages twice,' Carl said. He was bitter. I did not blame him. All the white hunters were bitter now, and the bearers sat in sullen groups on the verandah of the World Wild Life Fund regional office. In the old days they would lead a safari through the thick bush and out into the valleys where the cool wind of the night powdered the tracks of the rhino and they would smell the good smell of Africa and shoot every damn thing that moved. You could be drunk for a year on what you got for one safari. Now they worked as lollipop men on the busy crossing outside the Nairobi zoo or they carried easel and canvases for a man who painted bear cubs with big eyes and hung them up for sale on the railings of the Kenya National Park.

The sun was blinding now. The shadow thrown by the Kodak stand had shrunk to the size of one slat of a Venetian blind. Carl was packing up his matches. A girl from Sovereign Holidays was telling some tourists about the coach that would take them through a long stretch of glade and across the salt-plains to the place where they could buy models of big game carved out of teak. A boy scout shook a collecting box for the fund that helps lions with thorns in their feet.

'Where is the woman who sold postcards at twenty-five cents each, Carl?'

'Do you remember Simba, the kudu bull-elk who lived high in the timbered hills where we could never find him? Except for the day when you mistook him for a sandalwood tree and you hung your bush-jacket on his antlers?'

'I remember.'

'He came down to lick the ice-cream wrappers in the garbage can outside Dayville's on the road that leads to the game reserve. The woman who sold postcards was there and he trampled her to death.'

I hated her guts but not that much.

'Did you shoot him?'

'Yes – I got him at f5.6 in 1/125th of a second.'

Marx Twain

Russian film makers have turned the Dnieper River
into the Mississippi for a TV version of *The Adventures of
Tom Sawyer*, Russian style.

Standard

Tom appeared on the sidewalk with a bucket of white-wash and a long-handled brush. He surveyed the fence, and the gladness went out of his nature, and a deep melancholy settled down upon his spirit.

Twenty-seven point seventy-two metres of broad fence nearly three metres high! In a properly-constituted society that made intelligent use of its productive resources, a communal paint-spraying machine would have made short shrift of the task. Yet because the outlook of this peasant community remained essentially feudal, here, on a Saturday afternoon, it became necessary to exploit child labour in order to fulfil the whitewashing norm.

'Tarnation take it!' cussed Tom, and sitting on an upturned box he commenced to read his tattered copy of *The Condition of The Working Classes On the M—— River*.

Not for long. A window of the insanitary and tumbledown shack where Tom lived out his miserable existence was thrown up, and Aunt Polly appeared, brandishing a hickory switch.

'Law's sake, hang the boy, tormenting a body with his setting and reading and absorbing owdacious mischiefsome new ideas that a God-fearing post-colonist rural settlement jest can't abide! If you don't 'tend to your work this instant, Tom Sawyer, I've a notion to skin you alive!'

The flaying of boys, and the sale of their pelts to the oppressed Indians in exchange for wampum to deco-rate the idle necks of the womenfolk of the bourgeoisie, was at that time (the year 18—) a thriving trade in the region. Tom therefore rose with alacrity. Sighing, he dipped his brush and passed it along the topmost plank. He repeated the monotonous, soul-destroying opera-tion until Jim, the exploited child-slave, came trudging by with a heavy pail, singing 'Nobody knows de trouble I'b seen' in a melancholy bass. He was on his way to fetch water.

(Labour that should have been fruitfully exerted on the fields had perforce to be diverted to the drudgery of fetching water from the town pump, for the money raised from the sale of mulattos for riverboat-paddles, that should have provided an adequate drainage sys-tem, had been appropriated by the reactionary Judge Thatcher to spend on fineries for his daughter.)

Bringing water from the pump had always been hateful work in Tom's eyes before, but now it did not strike him so. He remembered that there was company at the pump: white boys like himself living under the lash of poverty, Negro children shackled with the invis-ible chains of political and social injustice, and other huddled masses. Perhaps they were even now drafting a resolution of solidarity with the Missouri One, as Injun Joe was described in the petition demanding a free pardon and an official enquiry.

'Say, Jim! I'll fetch the water if you whitewash some!' said Tom.

'I dassn't, Massa Tom. Until we been done change de existin' structure ob society whereby we can expropriate de political economy an' re-examine de whole capitalist meffod ob accumulation ob wealth an' white-washin' de fence, I's gwyne to be de slave' round heah an' do de fetchin' an' carryin'.'

'Shucks, Jim, you and me could change the existing structure of society with one hand tied behind our backs – but not if you're too scaredycat to do your fair share of the whitewashing!'

'I 'lows dat, Massa Tom, but missus she say ef I don' done fetch dat water, she'll hab my hide fo' boot-lebber!'

Jim shambled away. Tom's heart grew heavier as he thought of the day's educational activities on the river he had planned with the raft collective. And at this dark and hopeless moment an inspiration burst upon him. He took up his brush and went tranquilly to work.

The class-enemy Ben Rogers hove in sight presently; the very boy of all boys whose ridicule Tom had been dreading. Ben's heart was light, and he was eating an apple, and giving voice to a medley of sounds and shrieks, for he was personating a plantation-owner flogging a slave for stealing a mouthful of earth.

'Splat! Aaarrr! Nine hundred and eight-four. Splat! Aaarrr! Nine hundred and eighty-five . . . Hullo, Tom, old chap; you got to work, hey?'

No answer. Tom surveyed his last touch with the eye of a qualified artisan who has received adequate training at a state institution.

'Say, I'm going a-swimming,' said Ben. 'Don't you wish *you* could? But of course, you'd rather work, wouldn't you?'

Tom gave his brush another gentle sweep and surveyed the result as before. 'Why, hullo, Ben, I warn't noticing! What was that about work? This ain't work, this here is constructive recreation.'

'Looks like work to me.'

'Well it ain't, smarty-breeches. Tell you what Ben, gimme the core of your apple and I'll let you whitewash a whiles.'

Ben chomped thoughtfully.

'I don't think so, Tom. Didn't you say once that the bartering of a man's labour under the so-called "truck system" is a pestiferous influence which can only benefit the proprietor of the enterprise?'

'That wasn't me, it was Marx,' protested Tom.

'Seems to me it comes to the same thing,' said Ben, and carelessly flung his apple core into the whitewash bucket.

Reluctantly Tom took up his brush again. Other boys happened along every little while. Johnny Fisher brought him a dead rat and a string to swing it with; Billy Miller brought a kite in good repair; others brought blue bottle-glass, a couple of tadpoles, six fire-crackers, a brass door-knob. But upon Tom offering to trade a turn at whitewashing the fence for each and all of these treasures, his friends allowed that so rare and delightful a pastime should be costed at many times the money-worth of their humble possessions, and that Tom was exploiting himself and betraying his class by undercutting the market.

As Tom contemplated with dismay the far-reaching continent of still unwhitewashed fence, who should chance by but Huckleberry Finn, the deprived son of one of the township's victims of a socio-economic system which drove men to drink. Being under-privileged, Huck had only one possession, which he carried with him.

'Hullo, Huck! What's that you got?'

'Dead skunk for curing warts with.'

'I don't suppose you'd trade it for 'lowing you to whitewash this here fence?' said Tom without hope. 'Ain't every day you gets a chance to whitewash a fence, Huck.'

'Ain't every day I gits a chance to git quit of a dead skunk, neither!' said Huck; and to Tom's surprise and delight he took up the brush.

But Tom's pleasure soon turned to puzzlement when he saw that instead of painting the fence board by board as he was meant to, Huck was composing a huge whitewash circle.

'What are you doing, Huck? That's no way to whitewash a fence.'

'This here's a cake,' said Huck. With a flick of his brush he marked a dripping line through the circle. 'This here's what the manufacturer gits for the goods produced by the sweat of our labour; this here' – he marked off another dripping segment – 'is what the wholesaler gits; this here' – a smaller segment – 'is what the shopkeeper gits; and this here' – the smallest of the whitewash wedges – 'is the crumbs what's left for the working man who is the only true generator of all that there wealth. Tain't fair, Tom.'

'Quite the ragged-trousered philanthropist today, aren't we?' snapped Tom. 'Now s'posing you gets on with whitewashing that fence!'

But it was too late, for at that moment Aunt Polly arrived with her hickory stick, and when she saw what state her fence was in, she skinned Tom Sawyer alive.

Any Road Up

Thirteen of the nineteen public corporations such as the Electricity Board and British Telecom have agreed to put identification notices on holes their workmen dig in West Sussex roads.

Guardian

Seedrab regret any inconvenience caused by necessary roadworks.

In response to numerous inquiries from members of the public, Seedrab wish to make it clear that Seedrab is the acronym of the South-eastern Drainage Board, and hope that the necessary roadworks will be completed as soon as possible.

Seedrab thank motorists, pedestrians and residents of Jubilee Crescent for their patience and understanding while necessary roadworks were undertaken. These are now completed, but further roadworks in connection with the drainage renewal programme are anticipated in Sebastopol Terrace. Seedrab wish to apologize in advance for any inconvenience caused.

Metcon regret any inconvenience to residents of Jubilee Crescent caused by resurfacing following necessary roadworks by Seedrab.

In response to public inquiry, Metcon is the Metropolitan District Council Construction Services Dept, hence the initials MDCCSD still emblazoned on the steamroller, which is an old model. The reason the steamroller is still standing idly by, even though the tarmac-sprayer has done its work, is that Metcon has just heard on the grapevine that the hole in the road is about to be dug up again.

Metcon regret the inconvenience caused by their steamroller, tarmac-sprayer and other vehicles taking up most of the residents' parking bays in Jubilee Crescent, but they were definitely assured that work was to have started on the new hole in the road over a week ago, whereupon it would not have been a justified use of ratepayers' money to trundle all that equipment back to the depot only to have to trundle it back again. Metcon just cannot understand what is going on.

Seedrab regret any inconvenience caused while necessary roadworks are in progress in Sebastopol Terrace. They would point out, however, that they have completed their operations in Jubilee Crescent and that any subsequent cock-up in that particular thoroughfare is nothing to do with Seedrab.

While Metcon and Seedrab might have displayed a little more understanding of the problems involved before leaping into fluorescent print all over Jubilee Crescent

and Sebastopol Terrace, it has to be admitted that neither authority can be held responsible for the inconvenience caused to the public due to lack of relevant information and delay in commencing roadworks. This was due to both signwriters being on the holiday roster at the same time, owing to a flaw in administrative procedure which has since been rectified, and also to a flu epidemic among the labour force. Please watch this space.

Note: the above note should have been signed Nowsa.

Oh, sorry – North-western Sewage Authority.

In response to the numerous public inquiries, it is conceded that it must seem strange to the layman that Nowsa (North-western Sewage Authority) and Seedrab (South-eastern Drainage Board) should be digging holes in the same street. Reference to the attached map, however, will reveal slight overlapping of the two authorities in the shaded area which includes Jubilee Crescent. Nowsa further agrees, in fact Nowsa couldn't agree more, that with a bit of co-operation and forethought it should not have been necessary for a situation to obtain whereby Seedrab digs a hole in the road, Metcon fills it in and tarmacs it over, then along comes

Nowsa to start the whole rigmarole again from square one, which, by the way, it is hoped will be put in hand by Tuesday at the latest. Members of the public desirous of pursuing this matter further are referred to the district offices of Seedrab, where inquiries should be made of Mr Thornton, laughingly known as their co-ordinating officer.

Seedrab regret the continuing inconvenience caused to the public by the protraction of necessary roadworks in Sebastopol Terrace, but due to a fractured gas-main these works cannot be completed until appropriate action has been taken by Metcon, who up to press are denying that it is their pigeon. Turning to other matters, Seedrab do not know whether the public have been down Jubilee Crescent lately, but there is as libellous and damaging a statement to be found in Nowsa's latest on-site outburst as Seedrab has ever seen, and that is saying something. When Nowsa cast aspersions on the professional qualifications and abilities of Mr R. T. Horton (not Thornton – get your facts right, Nowsa), FICO, they happen to be talking about a gentleman who in addition to being a Past President of the Institute of Co-ordinating Officers at County level, was serving in local government while Nowsa's Mr Cousins was still sitting on his potty. Naturally, when a senior co-ordinating officer on one authority has as his opposite number on another authority a cretinous temporary Grade III clerk who cannot even spell people's names properly, breakdowns in communication will continue to arise.

Sticks and stones may break Nowsa's bones, but words will never hurt it. If Mr Horton of Seedrab would type his name on memoranda following standard practice, instead of scrawling it across the page like Mussolini or someone, errors of nomenclature would not arise. In acquainting the public with Mr Cousin's current status, Mr Horton is careful to omit that co-ordinating

254

holes in the road happens to be a Grade III appointment, and that is the only reason he himself is still
undertaking the task as a Grade 1+ appointee is that he
is too thick and stupid to do anything else. Nowsa
regrets the delay in commencing necessary roadworks
in Jubilee Crescent, owing to continued indisposition
among the labour force.

Metcon wish to inform the public that they do not
know where to start. Metcon would like to bang Seedrab's and Nowsa's heads together, honestly. There the
public has Mr Horton of Seedrab pouting and preening
like a turtle-dove, and he knows as much about co-
ordinating holes in the road as Metcon's backside. If Mr
Horton had anything but bread-paste between his ears,
it would have dawned on him by now that fractured
gas-mains are the responsibility of Britgascorp. They
are nothing to do with Metcon in any shape or form, so
the continuing inconvenience to the public in Sebastopol Terrace is all down to Seedrab. Turning to
Nowsa, if their workforce are all dying of flu thus
preventing them from starting necessary roadworks in
Jubilee Crescent after a fortnight of shilly-shallying,
how come they have got fifteen men in Chapel Road
digging a bloody great trench the length of the Maginot
Line?

Seedrab regret any ongoing inconvenience to the public in Sebastopol Terrace, owing to Metcon's Head of
Service not knowing his own job. Seedrab *know* fractured gas-mains come under the umbrella of Britgascorp. Short-arse, but notification has to be given to
them by the local authority, as any child of four could
tell you. Get on with it and stop buggering the public
about.

Nowsa regret the delay in commencing necessary
roadworks in Jubilee Crescent, owing to the limited
labour force available having been directed to Chapel

Road in order to co-ordinate hole-digging operations with similar roadworks being undertaken by Seedrab. Nowsa cannot help it if Seedrab have not, in the event, turned up.

God give Seedrab strength. Chapel STREET, you stupid berks!

Nowsa regret the invonvenience to the public caused by illiterate handwriting, but Nowsa have shown Seedrab's memo to five different people and they all agree it looks like Chapel Road. What else can the public expect from a so-called co-ordinating officer who is half-senile?

At least he is not half-blind. If Nowsa would care to step into Sebastopol Terrace and repeat that notice, Seedrab will take great pleasure in knocking Nowsa's head off.

Yeah? Seedrab and whose army? If Seedrab want to take on Nowsa, they know where Nowsa are to be found.

Really? Not in Jubilee Crescent, that's for sure. Or in Chapel Street either, come to that.

Metcon regret any inconvenience to the public caused by scuffling.

What I did on my Holidays

For my holidays this year we went, to the town of Venice. There, many canals are to be found, together with a big square, and, much ice-cream is to be had. But, there are no Dodgems. It not as good as Woburn Abbey.

Leaving home at 10 past 7 we arrived in the town of

Venice later. Our taxi driver was Mr Briggs. He vouch-safed, (I wish I coming with you) to which my erstwhile Father reply, (You can take my place if you like). The meaning of this Mysterious Remark was to be revealed ere an enchanting holiday was over.

Arriving in the town of Venice, we had Veal and Beetroot Salad followed by Cake, also as much Coca-Cola as you wanted. This on the plane before we got there, it was the Concorde. Arriving at our destination we travelled by Water Taxi to Journey's End, from whence our weary footsteps took us to our hotel. (What a dump) cried My Father, upon espying the Imposing Pile. The Water Taxi is not like an ordinary Taxi, it like a Boat. (I thought we supposed to overlook a Canal) he added for good measure, (This remind me of a Doss-house in the Caledonian Road).

(You were the one who wanted to come Venice so stop moaning) maintained My Mother sturdily, adding as an afterthought, (I would have been just as happy in Frinton, at least it not smell).

(If left to me I would have stayed at home and played Golf) snorted My Father by way of reply, adding with a Meaning Glance towards the Writer of this narrative, (And if he fall in Canal after all I have told him, I not fish him out). Thus the scene was set for a Holiday I shall never forget.

Came the Dawn. In the town of Venice, as I was to discover to my cost, they only have Bread for their breakfast, eggs and Bacon being unknown in this backward land. But, if, you go to the Shops, they always give you Sweets, if, you are on Holiday and, you buy something. This is because these primitive people do not have money. They, the Holidaymakers, have money, but They, the shopkeepers do not. Therefore, when you buy something, they do not give you change, they give you Sweets. Some of the aforesaid Sweets are red, some are blue, and others are purple, they like bubble-gum. Thus, I was able with God's Grace to survive that Fateful morning.

Little was said about the Matter until, My Parents came into my room, to see if I washed my hands before Lunch. I had not, but, I did not tell them, rather the reverse. Espying the Things I had bought upon my Bed, That Worthy sneered, (What all this junk?) Upon hearing my calm explanation, that, they were Presents, the Latter bellowed in voice stentorian (How much money you got left?) Upon hearing me boldy declare (Nothing) he go Purple. He same colour as my Sweets. (We been here only 10 minutes and, he has got through 5000 lire, it supposed to last him fortnight!) exploded the comical figure. His face a mask of evil he snarled (Look at all this rubbish, why he buy castanets? I suppose if we go to Spain next year he spend every penny on blessed toy gondolas!!!)

(Leave boy alone, for goodness sake, you always picking on him, pick pick pick) My Mother quavered staunchly, the blood draining from her lips.

(I will pick on him all right, I will pick him up and throw him out of bedroom window before I finished) swore My Father. So saying, he led the way to, the restaurant where we destined to have lunch, but, I not hungry.

(By all means leave your canelloni if it not to your taste, it only costing the best part of a day's earnings) observed My Relentless Father, whereupon he turned to His Spouse with the rejoinder (Or perhaps he'd prefer some spaghetti hoops?) This proved to be a cruel jest. I was Fated to have nothing to break my fast but fizzy water, a Morsel of Bread and Profiteroles, also a Peach.

After our frugal meal My Mother vouchsafed that she would like to sit on the Big Square and listen to the Band, but, My Father would have none of it. (You do not catch me paying £1 for thimble of coffee) declared the Miserly Fellow. After much discussion a compromise was reached, and, we went to see the Doge's Palace, where, many interesting dungeons are to be found, as well as the Torture Chamber, also many big drawings. Descending the golden staircase I meekly asked My Father if, I could have a pizza for supper. At this he gave a Hollow Laugh and groan (That bloody fantastic. You cart him all this way, you plonk him down in most beautiful city on God's earth, and all he can think about is Stomach). (We can't all be intellectuals) interjected My Mother with Dry humour. But, this not enough to stem My Father's Fury. Baring his teeth, he continue (At least he could use his eyes. When he came along Grand Canal yesterday, he not even look up, he just slouch in Water Taxi poking his finger through a Knothole). At this my Mother volunteered that, her Feet had swollen, also, that she wanted to spend a Penny, so, we went back to the Hotel to be received by our Genial Host. After a simple repast, I had Diarrhoea. So ended another Memorable Day.

On Monday we went to an Island, to see, them Blowing Glass, it like balloons but it is not, it is glass. I burn my Hand on furnace and, it was bandaged by, a Nun. On Tuesday, we went round many Churches, they have much painting, but not on the wall, it is on the ceiling. My Father keep saying (Look up, lad! Look up, lad!) Also (Is he mentally deficient?) On Wednesday, My Mother had a Blister, we sat in the big square at her request, pigeons being seen in large numbers. She had a Red Drink, whilst I had a Coke, and My Father had Whiskey. He go white when he get bill. (This cannot be the total, it the date) ran his statement.

On Thursday we went to, the Sands. Many ignorant people do not know that there are Sands in, the town of Venice, but, there are. It is called the Lido. The Lido is reached by boat, it pass an Island which is a Graveyard. In the town of Venice, when you are dead, the funeral is done by boats, strange to relate. Likewise, the fire brigade and, emptying the dustbins, but, we did not see any of this.

Our fruitful expedition to the Lido was uneventful, except, My Father offered me 1000 lire if, I could swim to Yugoslavia, but, I did not, and also, My Mother turn Bright Red all over. (I told you not to overdo it First Day) My Father crowed with scant sympathy for the Former, (You look like a Lobster). (Oh shut up, Miseryguts) My Mother riposted. They did not Speak again until Dinnertime when, I had Melon, a Plate of Chips and Mela Stragata, together with eighteen grapes. There are Dodgems at the Lido, but, My Father would not let me go on them. (This the Byzantine jewel of the Adriatic, not Battersea Fun Fair) quoth he darkly, with little meaning to my Good Self.

On Saturday, after tasting the Many Delights of the town of Venice the previous day, I ill. My Mother gasp shrewdly (This not just Diarrhoea, this Dysentry). My Father retort (With muck he been shovelling down, I surprised it not Bubonic Plague. Anyway, you not Fit to look after him, you are like a Lobster and also you are peeling like an Old Door, stuff this for game of candles, I am going to see if can get on tomorrow flight for Heathrow). With which he turned on his heel and Stormed Out.

My Mother said I could play quietly in my Room but, I did not. I went for Walk. Suffice to say that, My Father found me in Railway Station at, 9 p.m. My Mother was also among those present, saying (He wet through, he will catch Pneumonia). His Temples throbbing, My Father said monosyllabically (He been in Canal, he has probably got Every Disease Known To Man by now. We are going, to take the Next Train to Milan, and, we will take Pot Luck from there. If, there are only two cancellations on plane, we will leave him Behind.) Thus our Idyllic Holiday came to an auspicious end, and we said farewell to the town of Venice.

Polly Unsaturated

Chapter the Ninth

1

Why had he never thought of clearing out before?

Mr Polly was amazed and a little shocked at the superfluous criminality in him that had turned the Fishbourne Poulson centre into a blaze in Chapter the Eighth. But something constricting and restrained seemed to have been destroyed by that flare. The Fishbourne Poulson Centre, with its burned-out Carpet Centre, Music Machine Centre, Video Centre, Space Invaders Centre, Job Centre and Civic Centre, *wasn't the centre of the world.*

The compensation he expected to get from the Industrial Tribunal for unfair dimissal from the managership of the Poulson Centre Jazzy Jeans Centre after setting fire to it in the course of trying to commit euthanasia with an electric carving knife, would make all his arrangements humane and kindly and practicable. He would 'clear out' with justice and humanity, taking only the £8563 redundancy he had received when the Drapery Bazaar was taken over by the John Lewis Partnership back in Chapter the Fourth.

And he would go off along the underpass that led to Garchester, and on to Crogate and so to Tunbridge Wells. He would loiter by the way, and sleep in Expoconf Motor Inns or Travelama Budget Motels, and get an odd job here and there, and talk to strange people, and very likely get pulled in for questioning should any of them chance to be choirboys.

So the possibilities of the future presented themselves to Mr Polly.

2

A month later, on a profusely blooming sunny day, a
leisurely and contemplative figure in crash helmet,
jeans, bomber jacket and combat boots might have
been observed unhurriedly and serenely pedalling his
six-speed Tuff-Wheel Mongoose BMX bike along the
relief road between Uppingdon and Potwell.

Mr Polly knew that strictly speaking he should have
been observed unhurriedly and serenely striding along
with a knapsack on his back, and that the bit where he
impulsively tools off on his bike is in Chapter the Fifth.
But Mr Polly didn't care for walking and anyway he
was almost sure that in the movie, John Mills set off to
Potwell by bicycle. And so he adjusted his Xcaliber alloy
saddle-clamp and thought, 'Sod it, ol' man.'

After a moment for reflection he added: 'Definitely,
ol' man. Sod it.'

For such was Mr Polly's exuberance. For the first
time in many years he was leading a healthy human
life. He rediscovered this interesting world, about
which I am sorry to say many people go blind and
bored. He rode along country roads while all the birds
were piping and all the workmen were digging up
drains, and he looked at fresh new things such as the
Japanese optical instruments factory on the Old
Orchard Industrial Estate, and the propped-up blackboard against the electrified fence of buttercup Farms
(UK) Ltd, with the scrawled legend PICK YOUR OWN
STRAWBERRIES. FUDGE. CHILDREN'S MINI-ZOO.
MUSHROOMS. He came to country inns and sat at
rustic tables for unmeasured hours, waiting for a bar-
person to take his order for a half of keg lager and the
ploughman's lunch. He talked to wayside labourers and
to tramps, who explained to him how they were in
reality the rightful Duke of Edinburgh or Our Lord or
similar, who had had CB radio sets inserted into their
heads so that MI5 could monitor their thoughts.

'Itchabod,' said Mr Polly to himself. 'There's no going back now, ol' man, and that's a fact.'

3

It was about two o'clock in the afternoon, one hot day in May, when Mr Polly – still as unhurried and serene as a man may be whose BMX bike has been seized and squashed like a hedgehog by the original author of Chapter the Ninth whose justification was that Mr Polly's V-style forged goose-neck handlebars with single power clamp were taking the shape of things to come a bit too bloody far as regards bicycling – came at last upon that thatched inn sign with the cartoon Beefeater motif which is the trademark of British Heritage Caterers Ltd. He had arrived at the Potwell Inn, Steak Bars and Conference Centre, Regret No Coaches.

Presently, having taken his fill of wine by the glass, quiche and salad bowl in the Churchill Lounge, Mr Polly wandered across the car park overlooking the river. A gap in the wire mesh fence gave on to some concrete steps which led down to a landing stage where quite the plumpest woman Mr Polly had ever seen, in corduroy trousers and anorak, paraded up and down with a home-made picket sign, the slogan on which read COUNCIL LEISURE COMMITTEE OUT OUT OUT.

It was hard to say what there was about this tableau that made it so beautiful to Mr Polly, but it seemed to him to touch the scene with a distinction almost divine. He stood admiring the plump woman quietly for a long time.

Presently Mr Polly became aware of an agitated waving from some persons on the far bank of the river, and a distant howl of, 'Ooooover!'

Catching his eye the plump woman said, 'Darts team wanting the ferry. And there isn't a ferryman.'

'Could I?' asked Mr Polly, who had at once a fancy for

such congenial work.

'Have you a NUPE card? It's council-owned, see.'

'I could get one.'

'See Mr Coggins, branch secretary. You'll find him on the main door at the Geriatric Hospital, unless he's at an emergency conveners' meeting. Say Annie from the landing stage sent you.'

'When can I start work?'

'No idea friend. We're in dispute with the District Council Leisure and Amenities Committee. Until they rescind their ill-thought-out and totally partisan withdrawal of grant-in-aid to the Toddlers' Playbus, while continuing to underwrite middle-class activities such as the Operative Society, we maintain industrial action. That's street theatre co-ordinators, adventure playground supervisors, artificial ski-slope attendants, ferrymen, the lot.'

'No hurry,' Mr Polly said turning his eyes towards the river. 'While there's nothing doing I suppose I might do a bit of fishing.'

'You'll be lucky,' said the plump woman. 'River's polluted. Chemical works upstream.'

At which Mr Polly's soul grew black indeed. He had cut and run from all that was humdrum and squalid, yet the more thoroughly he made good his escape, the more humdrum and squalid his surroundings became.

The plump woman appeared to read his thoughts. 'Wait,' she cackled sardonically, 'till you see what's in store for you in Chapter the Tenth.'

Twist and Shout

Liverpool councillors are studying a report by the Corporation legal department revealing that two and a half years after a fund-raising campaign was launched for £40,000 for a statue to the Beatles, no more than £300 has been banked.

Daily Telegraph

At last night's meeting of the Clogthorpe District Council Leisure and Amenities Committee, under 'Any other business', Cllr Enoch Bulge (chairman) asked if he could canvass the views of members as to whether, in terms of publicity attracting the tourist trade and cashing-in generally, it would not be worth the borough's while to steal Liverpool's thunder and sling up a statue of Kevin Parkin while the great Merseyside metropolis was still dragging its feet as regards the Beatles.

On a point of information, Cllr Nepworth asked who Kevin Parkin was when he was at home.

The chairman said that Cllr Nepworth would probably know him better under the name of Sid Slime. Educated at Hugh Dalton Approach Comprehensive, he had risen from an apprentice window-cleaner to guitarist with the Hitler Youth Movement, a popular singing group. His latest LP, 'Armpit', had been No 6 in the charts and had been banned by the BBC.

Cllr Nepworth commented oh, him.

Opening the discussion, Cllr Tweedyman said that he would go to the foot of their (the Tweedyman family's) stairs. Suffering from a heavy cold, he had turned out on a bitterly cold night against doctor's orders to fight ill-advised proposals to close down the artificial ski-slope as further Danegeld to the Great God Economy. Having taken cognisance of the prohibitive cost of repairing the ski-slope consequent upon it having been used as a public toilet by a minority of Clogthorpe Wanderers supporters, he had conceded the debate with what he hoped was good grace and had been looking forward to making an early night of it with a glass of Lem-sip and a re-run of the Des O'Connor Show on the family video, when blow him, if the flaming chairman didn't start blathering on about putting up flaming statues to flaming punk stars. It was at times like these that Cllr Tweedyman asked himself why he bothered. Honestly, he kidded the Leisure and

265

Amenities Committee not.

Thanking Cllr Tweedyman for his typical and only-
to-be-expected courtesy in giving way on the ski-slope
issue when it had finally been got through his thick
skull that he was on a loser to nothing as usual, and
wishing him a speedy recovery from his indisposition,
Cllr Potter said that he heartily concurred with Cllr
Tweedyman in wondering why he bothered to remain
in local government. He could be best advised to take
the dignified way out and give up his council seat to a
younger man who would be more in tune with the
public taste.

Cllr Tweedyman, stating that he could probably give
the titles of more hit tunes, from 'Cruising down the
River' upwards or downwards as the case might be,
than Cllr Potter had had hot dinners, said he would
leave it to the electorate to judge whether he was in tune
with public taste or not. He stood second to none in
admiration of the Merseyside Mopheads who had been
mentioned by the chairman, particularly the late John
Lennon, who had rightly been compared with the late
Mozart. Cllr Tweedyman said that no man could
accuse him of not being with it. Whose idea had it been,
he would like to enquire of the Leisure and Amenities
Committee, for the flag over the Civic Centre to be
flown at half-mast in memory of the late Gracie Fields –
a proposal spitefully vetoed by the Vera Lynn faction
led by Cllr Potter?

Cllr Hopcraft said that speaking as one who had
voted with the Vera Lynn lobby on that occasion, he
had meant no disrespect to the late Gracie Fields. The
fact was that the late Gracie Fields was, with all due
respect, Rochdale's pigeon, not Clogthorpe's. By the
same token, the late John Lennon was Liverpool's
pigeon. On the other hand, when it came to erecting
statues or not erecting statues, Kevin Parkin, or Sid
Slime to use his stage name, was Clogthorpe's and no
other borough's pigeon.

Cllr Sludgeworth said but on the other hand yet again, Kevin Parkin alias Sid Slime was not dead.

Cllr Nepworth opined no, but he bloody well ought to be.

Intervening, the chairman said that the committee was getting nowhere at the double. The question was whether Clogthorpe should honour one of its sons by carving his name with pride and putting up a statue. They had the granite, they had the vacant plinth in Clogthorpe Park, they had sculptors in plenty over at the Art College. Was the answer an enthusiastic Yea or the usual faint-heart dog-in-the-manger Nay?

Cllr Elland said that while he was no square and had nothing against the be-bop, rock 'n' roll, call it what the Leisure and Amenities committee would, he was constrained to ask what Mr Slime had ever done for the borough. The answer was Sweet Francis Adams. He (Mr Slime) had left Clogthorpe hurriedly at the age of sixteen, consequent upon the police visiting his lodgings in Slaughterhouse Close and taking away certain substances, and he was nowadays residing in California. Sid Slime and the Hitler Youth Movement had never given a concert in Clogthorpe that Cllr Elland could recall, and had never taken up the standing invitation to advertise on the back page of *What's On In Clogthorpe and District*. His (Cllr Elland's) view was that he (Mr Slime) should be invited to go and take a running jump at himself.

Cllr Ackerman said that if having performed live in Clogthorpe was to be the criterion for having a statue put up, he would ask the committee to cast their minds back to the days of the old Clogthorpe Empire, when Mr Frank Randle had regularly played to full houses.

Cllr Sludgeworth said *Randle's Scandals*, Cllr Ackerman was going back a bit. Cllr Sludgeworth went on to ask, through the Chair, whatever happened to Issy Bonn.

Cllr Hopcraft asked what about what was his bloody

name now, the Street Singer?

Several members said Arthur Tracey.

Cllr Hopcraft concurred Arthur Tracey. Singing, Cllr Hopcraft went on to remind the committee that he (Cllr Hopcraft) was only a strolling vagabond, so good night pretty maiden to her.

Calling the committee to order, the chairman said that though these trips down Memory Lane were all very fine and dandy, Clogthorpe was a forward-looking borough and they were straying a long way from Sid Slime and the Hitler Youth Movement.

Cllr Nepworth said the further the better.

The chairman, ruling that while it was all right for toe-rags such as Cllr Nepworth to scoff from the side-lines, someone had to do the donkey-work of putting Clogthorpe on the map, then asked for views on the likely outcome of a public subscription for the venture in question. Liverpool had only managed to scrape £300 together for their lads, but they had probably gone about it the wrong way. What the chairman had in mind was involving the youth, on the basis that they were rolling in it these days.

Cllr Elland begged leave to remind the chairman that if he was talking about a Statue Fund, there already was one. It had been launched in aid of a suitable memorial for the late Alderman Stanley Dabthorpe, OBE, and the Fund stood, so far as Cllr Elland could recall off the top of his (Cllr Elland's) head, at ninepence in old money.

Cllr Ackerman said that the late Alderman Stanley Dabthorpe, OBE, now there had been a name to conjure with. The late Alderman Stanley Dabthorpe, OBE, had been a one. He had. By the left, he had been a lad and a half, had the late Alderman Stanley Dabthorpe, OBE.

Reminding the Committee that Alderman Stanley Dabthorpe OBE, had been lucky not to have served eighteen months in jail after that business over the

Civic Centre Annexe contract the chairman said that where the public did not give a monkey's for commemorating those who had selflessly devoted their lives to the public weal, they might feel differently towards their popular heroes, particularly the youth. The Statue did not have to be granite, it could be in some go-ahead material such as aluminium that the youth could identify with. What the chairman had in mind was launching an appeal, and seeing how it went, and perhaps inviting Mr Slime and the Hitler Youth Movement to Clogthorpe at the Council's expense to set the ball rolling.

Cllr Nepworth asked if there was any particular event at which Mr Slime and the Hitler Youth Movement might be expected to perform.

The chairman said that it was funny that Cllr Nepworth should have asked the above question, since his (the chairman's) daughter Noreen would be celebrating her eighteenth birthday in July and she was a particular admirer of Mr Slime and the Hitler Youth Movement.

Cllr Nepworth said yes, he (Cllr Nepworth) bloody well thought as much.

The chairman asked if Cllr Nepworth wished to repeat that particular insinuation outside the privilege of the committee room. Cllr Nepworth indicated that he did.

The meeting of the Leisure and Amenities Committee then went into private session in the cark park behind the Civic Centre.

The Thermo-Nuclear Property Boom

'I am by no means,' ventured Prendergast, Director with Responsibility for Refusing Mortgages, 'a cautious

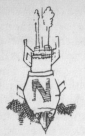

individual. Some of you will remember that when we considered extending loans to property built before 1938, I went overboard for the idea with the proviso that the said property should have a conventional sloping roof, a pebbledash frontage, two dinky little bay windows and a porthole in the front porch. But on this particular issue I believe – I stand open to correction – that we may be running before we can walk.'

The other members of the board of the Dunroamin, Erzanmine and Kosikot Building Society looked towards their chairman to see how he reacted to this outspoken statement. His face was a mask. All present began to fiddle with their gold pens and hum little tunes in a non-committal manner.

After seven or eight verses Jellicoe, Small Loans Applications, cleared his throat.

'Yes?' said the chairman encouragingly.

'I have a slight cough,' explained Jellicoe.

'You've started,' said the chairman, 'so you might as well finish.'

'Well,' began Jellicoe reluctantly. 'To some extent I agree with Prendergast. We must not bite off more than we can chew. But I too am not a conservative in the small-C sense. I supported the radical proposal to consider fifty per cent mortgages for selected terrace properties, on condition that they did not have flat roofs and that no terrace should consist of more than two houses. On the question before us, I am bound to say that there may be a case for taking a similar leap in the dark and seriously considering whether we should give the matter our consideration.'

'Hear hear,' said a member of the board without moving his lips.

'So you are proposing,' said the chairman, 'that the Dunroamin, Erzanmine and Kosikot Building Society should underwrite the neutron bomb?'

'I didn't say that at all,' protested Jellicoe.

The chairman turned to Weatherby, Actuarial Tables with Special Reference To Those Over The Hill At Forty.

'You haven't spoken yet, Weatherby.'

'I've lost my voice, sir.'

'In a word, what's your opinion?'

'I agree, sir,'

'With whom – Prendergast or Jellicoe?'

'With both, sir. Up to a point. As Prendergast says, or implies, or as I understand him to imply, it would be unusual for the Society to extend a loan on a bomb. But as Jellicoe says, or seems to be suggesting, or at any rate creates the general impression of having suggested, the particular bomb on our agenda would seem to have considerable advantages for the building societies. Subject to survey, of course.'

'Strike that from the record,' said Prendergast and Jellicoe simultaneously. 'It is not a fair summary of our views.'

The meeting relapsed into silence. The boardroom clock ticked the minutes away. A fly buzzed around the mahogany table and settled on the nose of Appletree, Forclosures, who hesitated to brush it away in case the chairman thought he was calling for attention.

After an hour, it was Manningham, Director In Charge Of Thinking Up Smart Excuses Why The Mortgage Rate Shouldn't Be Reduced, who spoke.

'I'm retiring on Friday, so I'm going to stick my neck out,' he began recklessly. 'As I understand it, and I would have to study the relevant documents in detail before setting myself up as an authority one way or another, the neutron bomb may be employed by NATO in any contingency occasioned by or happening through War Invasion Act of Foreign Hostilities (whether War be declared or not) Civil War Rebellion Revolution Insurrection or Military or Usurped Power, including Riot and Civil Commotion. According to the report of the Society's surveyor, the explosion kills or disables any householder within two thirds of a mile, yet leaves his property intact. Said property, in the absence of any arrangements being made by surviving executors, would automatically be foreclosed by and come into the possession of the building societies. In a word, it is the first bomb ever devised that protects our investments.'

'That's your opinion, is it?' the chairman asked.

'I didn't say it was my opinion, Mr Chairman, I am merely quoting what has been said to me.'

The chairman peered under the boardroom table, where Appletree, Foreclosures, was pretending to tie his shoelace.

'This is your field, Appletree. What's your view?'

'I've only just come into the room, sir. I'm sorry I'm late, but I had to go to the dentist.'

'Nevertheless, I am asking you whether we should grant the applicant an eighty per cent mortgage, subject of course to the usual conditions and mandatory security in the form of a massive endowment policy, on a new-fangled bomb that does not have a conventional tiled roof?'

'I have to admit, sir,' confessed Appletree, 'that to a qualified extent I support Manningham. And I'm not only saying that because I'm emigrating to Australia next week. We have, to a limited degree, to move with the times. It may be true that the old-fashioned H-bomb has been tried and tested, and there is no danger of it becoming subject to a council demolition order, but it doesn't half play havoc with property. The way I look at it, sir, if a mortgagee's dwelling-house has been flattened, he loses all incentive to keep up his loan payments. And the society, of course, has lost its security because of the Pestilence Famine and Act of God clause in the insurance policy.'

'So you support the neutron bomb?'

'No, sir. I think the NATO alliance should build up a stockpile of medium-range bungalows.'

'I think,' said the chairman, since no one else ventured an opinion, 'that we'd better have a look at the surveyor's report. Who has it?'

The surveyor's report had been circulating rapidly around the table as in a game of Pass the Parcel. It finished up in the unfortunate hands of Cabthorpe, Director With Responsibility For Telling People They Can't Have A Mortage Until The Place Has Been Completely Gutted And A Damp Course Put In.

'Read it out, Cabthorpe.'

'I've forgotten my glasses, Mr Chairman.'

Willing hands thrust horn-rimmed spectacles, monocles and magnifying glasses in Cabthorpe's direction. Pointing out that the surveyor's report did not necessarily agree with his own views, whether in whole or in part, he commenced to read.

'Report on All That Bomb Situate and Known as the Neutron Bomb. Without prejudice. Errors and omissions excepted. Report submitted subject to the conditions of – '

'Get on with it,' the chairman invited tersely.

'"The bomb is of the missile type, freehold, with accommodation for a nuclear warhead, but no garage or garden. It was built in 1978 . . ."'

'That's a point in its favour,' murmured the chairman. 'Those Edwardian bombs may have looked all very quaint and charming, but try getting one rewired!'

'I was not able to inspect the interior of the bomb since there was no access available, but the caretaker informed me that it was capable of inducing fits, heart failure, third-degree burns, radiation sickness and death within a radius of approximately 1430 yards, while causing little damage to property beyond dislodging slates and guttering. The exterior, or casing, is made of metal. It was free from rust and no rising damp was visible. The bomb does not appear to be connected to the mains water supply . . .'

'That's enough,' said the chairman. 'What is the view of the board?'

'Hear hear,' chorused the directors.

'I believe the applicant is a government,' the chairman continued. 'Has it ever applied for a loan before?'

'Often,' said Prendergast. 'But not from us.'

'Then we should give the matter some thought. Of course, we would have to be satisfied that the neutron bomb is as structurally sound as it appears to be from our surveyor's report. I suggest the applicant should be advised to apply to its bank for a bridging loan, and we will consider advancing the monies required after the bomb has been dropped on Russia. Subject to re-survey, availability of funds, contingencies, et cetera et cetera. Agreed?'

'In principle,' chanted the directors of the Dunroamin, Erzanmine, and Kosikot Building society.

Matthew, Mao, Luke and John

The first Chinese edition of the Bible to be printed in
China in more than two decades is expected to be
printed next year.

Daily Telegraph

In the beginning, Chairman God created the people's republic. And the people's republic was without form, and void; and darkness was upon the face of the deep. And Chairman God said, Let there be a significant improvement in living conditions, and there was a significant improvement in living conditions . . .

'What shall I put instead of Canaanites, Hittites, Amorites, Perizzites, Hivites and Jebusites?' asked Ming.

'Put broad masses,' said Peng. 'And stop interrupting my train of thought. I want to break the back of this *Song of Solomon* before I go to my re-education class.'

'You poor sod,' said Ming. 'Being re-educated again, eh? What for this time?'

'Handwriting. You remember that Koran I translated last year? They only went and printed Percival Chairman Allah all through instead of Merciful Chairman Allah, didn't they?'

'Mistake anyone could make,' sympathized Ming. 'They give you these flaming clapped-out whitewash brushes to work with, then start moaning because they can't read your ideographs. Still, just goes to show you, you can't be too careful.'

They worked on in silence for a while. Peng wrote in delicate flourishing strokes, 'Stay me with flagons, comfort me with apples, for I am sick of love,' then crossed it out and substituted, 'Provide essential supplies, for a worker who is diseased from malnutrition cannot function efficiently.'

Ming, sucking his brush, said, 'It still doesn't look right.'

'What doesn't look right?'

'"I am come down to deliver them out of the hand of the Egyptians, and to bring them up out of that land unto a land flowing with milk and honey, unto the place of the broad masses."'

'You stupid berk,' said Peng, annoyed at being distracted again. '"Course it doesn't look right. You've put Egyptians, haven't you?'

'What's wrong with putting Egyptians?'

'We're only trying to trade with the bastards, aren't we? Just wait till the Gyppos tell Chairman Hua what you've been writing about them in the Big Black Book – your clogs won't touch the ground, matey.'

'What shall I do, then?'

'Play it safe,' advised Peng. 'And while you're about it, for Chairman God's sake don't let that land-flowing-with-milk-and-honey stuff go through. Suppose someone gets up and reads that out at a collective farm discussion group, and it happens to coincide with a temporary shortage of dairy products caused by an

imperfect understanding of the workings of centralism? They'd be denouncing you on flaming wall posters, mate.'

Ming thanked Peng for the tip and placed a new sheet
of ricepaper alongside his open Bible.

'How's this?' asked Ming at last. '"I am come down to
deliver them out of the hand of the imperialist paper
tigers and the despised landlord class responsible for
the ruthless economic exploitations and political oppres-
sion of the proletariat, and to bring them unto a good
land, unto a land where the apparatus for the distribution of goods can function smoothly only if there is
a proper understanding of the workings of centralism
at every lever, unto the place of the broad masses."'

'It'll do,' said Peng. 'What's Chinese for "breasts like
pomegranates"?'

*And Chairman God made a commune eastward in the province of
Eden, and there he put the peasants. And out of the ground made the
people's efforts to grow every tree that is consistent with the socialist
transformation of agriculture, and good for food; the tree of life also
in the midst of the commune, and the tree of knowledge of correct
ideology and mistaken ideology . . .*

'So much for Aaron's Rod,' said Ming. 'What shall I do
next?'

'Do what you bleeding like, mate,' said Peng. 'But
push my elbow once more while I'm trying to work out
a phonetic compound for "Tell it not in Gath, publish it
not in the streets of Peking," and you'll get this flaming
inkpot right in the mush.'

'Shall I carry on with the Long March?'

'Long March, what Long March?' asked Peng in
some alarm. He grabbed the batch of manuscripts that
Ming had placed in the out-tray and skimmed through
it feverishly.

'Chairman God Almighty!' breathed Peng, as he
struck a match and carefully set fire to Ming's transla-

276

tion. 'If this Book of Exodus had gone through the way you've written it, we'd have got 25 years' rehabilitation apiece! Rewrite it, and this time make the journey through the wilderness to the promised land sound more of a doddle.'

'The Short March, shall I call it?' asked Ming.

'The Short March through the suburbs, much better,' said Peng.

Chairman God is my Shepherd, I shall not want,

   He layeth down the general line and general policy of the people's revolution as well as various specific lines for work and specific policies,

   He leadeth me beside the still waters,

   He reviseth my soul,

   He correcteth my mistaken ideas for his name's sake

   Yea, though I experience changes in society due chiefly to the development of internal contradictions between the productive forces, I will fear no evil, for thou art with me.

   Thy theory and ideology they comfort me . . .

'What shall I put instead of frogs?' asked Ming.

Peng threw down his brush in exasperation.

'Can't you see I'm trying to concentrate?' he snarled. 'Here I am doing my damnedest to draw a pictograph of Babylon the Great, the mother of harlots and abominations of the earth so it doesn't come out looking like Hong Kong, and you're rambling on about bloody frogs!'

'Yes, but what shall I put?' persisted Ming.

'Put frogs, you stupid berk!'

'Will Chinese readers know what we're talking about?'

'Of course Chinese readers'll know what we're talking about!' screamed Peng. 'We have frogs, don't we? We have millions of the buggers! It's not only the decaying rump of the discredited French Colonel Empire that can afford frogs, believe you me!'

'Yes, but we don't have plagues of frogs, do we?' asked Ming.

277

'Oh, *plagues* of frogs,' said Peng, partly mollified, 'You didn't say *plagues* of frogs. No, 'course we don't have *plagues* of frogs, because inspired youth cadres working in unity and co-operation with the frog-sprayers' collective wiped out the little sods, didn't they? What you doing then, the seven fat years and the seven lean years?'

''S right,' said Ming.

'I should scrub out the lean years, if I were you,' said Peng. 'Make them two sets of fat years, and do them in fives, not sevens.'

'No plagues of frogs?'

'No plagues of frogs, and don't bother me again, I'm getting to the tricky bit.'

'What tricky bit?' asked Ming.

'This New Testament bit,' said Peng, with a worried frown. 'Personality cult problem there, I reckon. Plus there's a strong implication of the outmoded hereditary principle. If you ask me, Ming, I think we ought to miss that bit out altogether.'

The wolf also shall form a committee with the lamb, and the leopard shall strengthen relationships and exchange information with the kid; and the calf and the young lion and the fatling resolutely carry out orders; and a little child shall represent our collective leadership . . .

Death in the Afternoon

Following Clogthorpe's Day of Shame, when Clogthorpe supporters, many of them behaving like animals, went on the rampage through the Poulson Shopping Mall after their 8–1 trouncing at the hands of Sludgeboro' New Town Albion, an emergency meeting of the Clogthorpe Wanderers directors was held on Monday at the Hugh Dalton Approach ground.

Opening the discussion, club chairman, Cllr Tweedyman, said he knew it was small comfort, but there was one good thing to be said. Unlike the biggest majority of soccer hooligans, the vicious minority who were dragging Clogthorpe's name in the mire had at least done it on their doorstep and not on somebody else's.

Mr G. Leadbetter said that was only because they were barred from visiting any other ground in the country, not to mention Europe and much of South America, for the rest of the season. If they were going to behave at home fixtures like what they had been in the habit of behaving away, namely baring their bottoms at old age pensioners and overtuning cooked Halal meat stalls, then he, Mr G. Leadbetter, gave up.

Mr R. J. Netherby said they wanted birching.

Mr D. Robarts said they wanted more than birching, they wanted to be flogged in public. Public flogging at half-time would be quite an attraction. Mr Robarts also thought that hot-dog sales would encourage the family audiences they were after.

Saying that Clogthorpe District Council was not empowered under any bye-law known to him to authorize unilateral corporal punishment, even on an experimental basis, Cllr Tweedyman added that hot-dogs had been tried and an unrepresentative element had pelted the referee with them.

The Rev L. B. Shadd said that while he held no brief for mindless hot-dog throwing, the incident had been blown up out of all proportion by the sensation-hunters of the *Clogthorpe Mercury*. To set the record straight, what had happened was that teenagers from socially-deprived areas such as the Clement Attlee Overspill Conurbation had bought hot-dogs in good faith and found them to be smothered in German mustard, instead of the steamed onions to which they felt entitled. They had flung their hot-dogs at the referee's as a cry for help. The one who had nearly put the referee's eye out had since apologized in court. There was no single answer to the problem, but there was a crying need for a proper amenity and leisure centre where these youths could let off steam.

Mr R. J. Netherby said they had let off enough steam at the Poulson Shopping Mall to run a bloody industrial laundry for a week. The Job Centre windows had been smashed in, the Gas showroom looked as if a tornado had been through it, the Kentucky Fried Chicken and Dayville's had been used as public urinals and as for the Queen Mother's Eightieth Birthday Commemorative Tree, God knew where it was now, because Mr R. J. Netherby certainly didn't. They didn't want amenity and leisure centres, they wanted a short sharp shock.

Mr D. Robarts said he was convinced that public floggings were the answer, despite the legal quibbles raised by the chairman. What was needed was for the ringleaders to be stripped bare, hung up by the heels from the goalpost crossbars, and lashed with whips of plaited wire until the blood ran down their backs.

On a point of order, Mr G. Snubbin said that anatomically speaking the blood would be running up their backs if they were hanging by the heels, although he would concur with Mr D. Robarts that the blood would be running in a downward direction. However, he had not come to this emergency meeting to quibble. He agreed with Mr Netherby that a short sharp shock was required, and Mr Robarts had made one practical suggestion as to how such a shock could be administered. That was all right so far as it went, but some of these thugs needed a more permanent reminder that Clogthorpe had had it up to here with their senseless violence. They should have a letter H for hooligan branded on their foreheads with red hot irons, and then they should be made to do PT at an attendance centre every Saturday afternoon for the rest of their lives.

Mr D. Robarts said yes, and if they missed just one appearance they should be hung in chains along Hugh Dalton Approach. Cllr Tweedyman was a member of the District Council Highways Committee: did he think the Clerk of Works' department could rustle up a few dozen wooden crosses like what they had had in *Ben Hur*? If not, they would have to make do with the existing lamp posts.

Noting the suggestions made so far, Cllr Tweedyman said he would like to get away from the retribution element and on to prevention, because if Clogthorpe Wanderers didn't put their house in order before very long, they might just as well shut up shop and sell the Hugh Dalton Approach park for housing development, as there would not be a team in the world that would play with them.

The Rev L. B. Shadd said he was glad the discussion was reaching a more constructive stage. It would be sad if the directors did no more at this meetng than feed the prejudices of the *Clogthorpe Mercury* leader-writer, with whom bringing back the stocks was becoming an obsession. The Rev L. B. Shadd would like to feel that they had a measure of understanding for their supporters, many of whom came from one-parent families.

Mr L. Butterworth said he could well believe it, and he had a pretty good idea which parent it was that the young so-and-sos lacked.

Cllr Tweedyman said he would like to review the precautionary measures being taken up to press. For a kick-off, no visiting supporters whatsoever were allowed into the park – a rule so strictly enforced that last week the police had refused entry to the Sludgeboro' New Town Albion manager, for which almighty cock-up he (Cllr Tweedyman) had had to apologize most humbly. Second off, all Clogthorpe supporters were herded into an electrified cage at the Canal Lane end. They were made to hand in their boots, and they were also put up against a wall and frisked. Suspected troublemakers were thrown into a special pit protected by spiked iron bars, from which they couldn't even see the game. Buckets of pigswill were thrown over them at intervals to keep them quiet. Third off, as the fans left the ground, hosepipes were turned on them as a matter of course. The County Chief Constable, however, was now asking for further steps to be taken to defuse the escalating violence situation. Moats filled with piranha fish had been put forward but there was always the danger of the linesman falling into them.

Mr D. Robarts said that instead of digging moats, what the club should do was, they should build a rack similar to the one used to extract a confession from Guy Fawkes. When handing in their boots, supporters would be given a numbered ticket, and the one drawing the unlucky number would be put in a dungeon and stretched.

Mr L. Butterworth said they could hang, draw and quarter their supporters it would not make a ha'porth of difference. There would always be violence so long as there was one supporter left standing in the Canal Lane end electrified cage.

Mr R. J. Netherby said he was afraid that was the case. They should take a tip from West Ham, who were allowed to play their European Cup winners' Cup game only on condition that no spectators of any shape, form or kind were allowed through the turnstiles.

Cllr Tweedyman said he was glad Mr Netherby had mentioned the Hammers, because playing the rest of the season's fixtures behind so to speak closed doors was something that he (Cllr Tweedyman) had been brooding on for many a long hour.

Mr L. Butterworth said it was a good idea in principle, but what if the fans broke through the barbed wire and got into the ground?

Cllr Tweedyman said they needn't necessarily play at Hugh Dalton Approach. They could make use of some secret venue such as that disused airfield up near Colliery Marshes. The *Clogthorpe Mercury* would be asked to kindly not report the game, so no one would know it had taken place.

Mr G. Leadbetter asked what if the fans found out where their team was playing? It would be like World War II.

Cllr Tweedyman said he had taken the Chief Constable's advice on that. Both sides would wear plain strip and stocking masks, so that they would be impossible to identify. The fans, if they managed to get through the landmines surrounding the pitch, would not know whether they were watching Clogthorpe Wanderers or Sheffield Wednesday. This might not stop them cutting a mindless swathe of destruction through the Poulson Shopping Mall later, but at least they would not be bringing their team into further disrepute.

Mr D. Robarts said that was one way out of their dilemma, but he would like to see a simpler solution tried out first. He was thinking in terms of a device he had taken cognizance of in an illustrated history of torture, namely the Iron Maiden . . .

William the Red

The attack of Marxist thinkers and writers on education in Britain today deserves serious attention, according to a special report.

The Times

'Now I don't want you under me feet today, William,' said Mrs Brown, carefully arranging a vase of flowers. 'Some very important members of the National Front are coming for tea and we shall want the house to ourselves.'

William favoured his mother with one of the withering glances for which he was famous.

"Spec you'll be making bombs,' he said darkly. "Spec you'll be teachin' 'em how to rig up a booby trap out of 88 parts nitroglycerin an' five parts potassium nitrate.'

William's father, with an audible sigh, lowered his copy of *Did Six Million Really Die?*

'Don't they teach you anything at school?' groaned Mr Brown. 'Eighty-eight and five come to ninety-three! You've missed out the seven parts neutralizing agent! No wonder you're always blowing up the greenhouse!'

'Which,' said Mrs Brown firmly, 'will be paid for out of your pocket money. And I won't have you going about the village telling everyone that your home is a bomb factory. If it is, it's your own doing. We on the extreme right seek to overthrow the Government by peaceful means.'

The arrival of Ethel with a cakestand piled high with iced buns put William in a quandary. Much as he loved a political argument, his fondness for iced buns was legendary.

'I s'pose,' he said gloomily, 'that all that food is for the fascist degenerates who are tryin' to drive a wedge through the solidarity of the toilin' masses by spreadin' race-hatred an' – an' – poisonin' people's brothers' minds?'

The last was a shaft at his brother Robert who had recently placed a notice reading, 'FOR SALE TO WHITES ONLY' on the windscreen of his two-seater. There had been a painful scene when he had discovered that some mysterious person had 'improvised' upon his handiwork by adding: 'FASHIST SKUM PRIFFERED.'

'Yes, it is!' flared Ethel. 'And for goodness' sake go and wash your face! Himmler's nephew will be here in a moment to take me to tennis, and I don't want him to think we're housing a – a – juvenile squatter!'

William quelled his sister with a basilisk stare.

'Ol' Marx wun't have kep' all that food to himself,' said William smoulderingly. 'Ol' Marx would've said that jus' 'cos a person doesn't go round scrawling swastikas on people's gates it doesn't mean to say he's got to live on bread an' water. Ol' Marx . . .'

'Oh, do be quiet, William,' said his mother wearily.

William's gift of eloquence was known and feared in his family circle.

A few moments later, having incurred his father's wrath by asking him why he didn't work down a coalmine if he thought the miners were so grossly overpaid, William dejectedly kicked a tin-can along the footpath leading to the Old Barn.

'Jus' wait till we get worker control, that's all,' muttered William sternly to himself. 'Jus' wait till they all come to realize the fundamental proposition of ol' Marx's economic interpretations of history. 'Spec they'll come to me an' Ginger an' Henry an' Douglas beggin' for mercy. 'Spec they'll want us to let 'em out of prison just 'cos they di'n't understan' the self destructive nature of capitalism.'

William brightened as he saw the hammer and sickle fluttering bravely from the roof of the Old Barn. That meant the Outlaws were waiting for him to deliver his lecture on 'Zur Kritik der Politischen Okonomie'. William, of whom it could not be said that modesty was a failing, was confident that he had mastered his subject. His history master, Mr Tonks, was a member of the International Workers' Ideological Platform, and William was his star pupil.

But William reckoned without the exuberant impatience of his fellow-Outlaws.

"S no use jus' *talkin'* about it,' interrupted Ginger after he had been in full flow for an hour and a half. 'Anyone can *talk* about gettin' worker control an' that. 'S all right you jus' *talkin'*. What we want is action.'

'An' I s'pose ol' Marx di'n't talk about it?' retorted William, waxing satirical. 'I s'pose ol' Marx was deaf an' dumb too. I 'spec they jus' spoke in sign language. I 'spec all the Russians understood sign language, so they knew jus' when to overthrow the guv'ment.'

It was a powerful argument but the Outlaws were not impressed. They were bored with theory, and as Ginger had rightly surmized, they craved action.

'On the television news,' suggested Henry, 'they kidnap somebody an' hold them to ransom until the guv'ment agrees to release the others from prison.'

'What others?' asked William.

'The rest of the gang.'

'Oh, I see,' riposted William with withering sarcasm. 'Up till now, I di'n't know the rest of the gang was even in prison. Up till now I thought we were all here. Up till now I thought there was jus' me, you, Ginger and Douglas. I 'spec I was wrong. I 'spec I jus' can't count.'

William's unassailable logic was lost on the Outlaws.

'We could kidnap Violet Elizabeth Bott,' suggested Douglas.

'She'd prob'ly scream,' said Ginger doubtfully. Brightening considerably, he added: 'We could always derail the 4.17 from Hadleigh an' take hostages.'

William frowned. His authority was being undermined. But William was well versed in the art of leadership. Instinctively, he knew that in order to lead it was sometimes necessary to follow.

"Course,' he said airily, 'if we did want to do somethin' to bring the goal of a true socialist democracy a bit nearer, we could always go an' disrupt the National Front meetin' that's taking place under our own noses. But 'course, I 'spec you'd rather go an' kidnap Violet Elizabeth Bott, then she'll scream and scream and be sick and you'll all get caught an' put into prison.'

The shrewdly-phrased proposition had the desired effect. There were immediate murmurs of assent. Only Ginger, who was anxious to save face, raised the slightest objection.

'How will we go about disruptin' it?' he asked feebly.

'How do I know?' countered William fiercely. 'We'll disrupt it, that's all. I don't s' pose ol' Lenin knew 'xactly what he was going to do when he went back to Russia on that sealed train. He jus' knew he had to go an' disrupt something, 'stead of jus' kidnapping people who'd scream and scream and be sick.'

Some ten minutes later the Outlaws were to be seen marching purposefully along the village street in the direction of the Brown household. The 4.17 from Hadleigh, its passengers mercifully unaware of the fate from which William's saturnine diplomacy had saved them, had just steamed into the tiny station. A solitary passenger, a distinguished-looking, serge-suited individual with a gleaming dome, pince-nez and an Imperial beard, had stepped off the train and was making his way uncertainly towards the village street.

William stopped dead in his tracks. He gripped Ginger's arm so tightly that the invincible Outlaw could not forbear a wince. 'I mus' be dreamin'!' gasped William.

'When you've quite finished with people's arms—' began Ginger indignantly. But William continued in a state of high excitement.

'Don't you reccernize him? It's ol' Lenin!'

'Ol' Lenin?' echoed Henry and Douglas in unison. 'It can't be!'

'It *is* ol' Lenin! He's 'xactly like that portrait of him in the School Hall! 'S easy to see why he's here,' added William, his fertile imagination working overtime. 'He's done all he can to bring about Socialism and that in Russia, so. now he's come over here to spread dissatisfaction an' revolution among the oppressed workers!'

'Wish we could take him to the National Front meetin',' said Ginger wistfuly. 'Ol' Lenin'd disrupt it all right.'

'I've already thought of that,' retorted William with immense dignity.

By now the stranger was level with the Outlaws. William with the hideous smirk which he fondly imagined was an ingratiating smile, stepped boldly in his path.

''Scuse me, sir,' said William. 'I'm Brother Brown, an' these are Brother Douglas an' Brother Ginger an' Brother Henry. We're wondering if you'd like to come an' have tea after your long journey.'

'Oh, have you been sent to meet me?' beamed the bearded stranger. 'How very kind!'

'Oh, dear,' wailed Mrs Brown. 'I do hope nothing's happened to Mr Urquart-Jones! Perhaps he's dozed off on the train and gone beyond his station!'

'It's none of my business, dear,' said the Vicar's wife, to murmurs of consternation from the pillars of the village society assembled in the crowded drawing room, 'but as organizer of our little National Front branch, I do think you might have arranged for him to be met.'

'After all,' put in Mrs Bott, "'e's ever such an important person, what's put 'imself out to travel all the way from London.'

'Oh, dear!' murmured Mrs Brown again. Anxiously she glanced out of the window. Then her brow cleared. The distinguished guest accompanied by William and those disreputable friends of his, was even now walking up the drive.

'Dear lady!' boomed the welcome latecomer. 'A thousand apologies! I forgot your address and would doubtlessly never have found you but for the kind assistance here of these young gentlemen! I see we have iced buns. The least we can do is invite them to a substantial tea!'

The Outlaws needed no further bidding. They fell on the iced buns like the starving peasants of pre-revolutionary China.

Without further ado, their protégé launched into his speech. 'Ladies,' he began. 'When Asians in receipt of £600 a week in State benefits ask for more welfare handouts, it is surely the time to cry halt . . .'

William nearly choked on his iced bun. Surely ol' Lenin was getting a bit revisionist in his old age? Surely none of that stuff about sending the immigrants packing was in the Communist manifesto?

William hastily swallowed the last crumb and rose to his feet. Then he noted that although the huge mound of iced buns had vanished without trace, there was an equally huge mound of chocolate eclairs.

As ol' Lenin commenced a diatribe about Social Security scroungers, William reached out with both hands and seized two eclairs, then sank back into his chair with an air of contentment.

Marxism was the future. But eclairs were now.

THE END